BEATING THE BIOLOGICAL CLOCK

Pamela Armstrong started her career as a journalist with Capital Radio where she presented 'London Today' and reported 'Operation Drake', spending six months sailing from Panama to Papua New Guinea. She came to national prominence on ITN's 'News at Ten' before moving on to present her own programme for the BBC and anchor BBC's 'Breakfast Time' and 'Daytime Live'. She is currently broadcasting on BBC World Service Television. She is the author of a book on the menopause – *The Prime of Your Life* – published in Headline's Health Kick series.

GW00674275

BEATING THE BIOLOGICAL CLOCK

The Joys and Challenges of Late Motherhood

Pamela Armstrong

HEADLINE

First published in 1996 by
HEADLINE BOOK PUBLISHING

10 9 8 7 6 5 4 3 2 1

ISBN 0 7472 7814 8

Typeset by Avon Dataset Ltd, Bidford-on-Avon, Warks

Printed and bound in Great Britain by
Mackays of Chatham PLC, Chatham, Kent

HEADLINE BOOK PUBLISHING
A division of Hodder Headline PLC
338 Euston Road
London NW1 3BH

Contents

Although their conversation was private, I managed to hear most of it.

I had to lean forward at a sharp angle to catch the words. I pretended to be interested in the passing scenery. The three men were absorbed. Through the roar of the train I heard her story.

She had lived with a friend of one of the men for seven or eight years. It had been a good relationship till she wanted children. At this point he resisted. They continued to battle, but her longing never left her, and he never relented. So, first, she ran off with a local ne'er-do-well, and then, for a long time afterwards, had a string of unfortunate affairs combined with some pretty wild living.

Eventually, much later in life, she settled into a steady and happy, though childless, relationship. She stayed in touch with her original partner and they saw each other occasionally. The last time he'd seen her had been a shock. She had been unwell – so unwell and off colour, in fact, that she had gone to the doctor.

'I'm not surprised you're a bit out of kilter,' the doctor had said. 'You're seven months pregnant.' She was 46.

This book is dedicated to that woman, whoever and wherever she is.

INTRODUCTION

Vintage Motherhood

Women have children late in life for a huge variety of reasons. There is little else I can tell you about the life of the woman described in the dedication, except to say it resonates with so many older mothers' stories. Basic themes appear again and again. Often there is longing. Usually there is delay – and then, perhaps at the eleventh hour, the child is born. Our stranger on a train could so easily be the Everywoman of today for older mothers.

In reality, she is only one of a growing band. 'Baby boom time for Britain's 40-somethings'; 'Single, over 40 and keen to be a mother'; 'Motherhood going out of fashion for young women' – these are just some of the headlines that announced the official arrival of news that the woman in the street has known for years. Finally, the statisticians have caught up. Women are delaying having their families longer and longer. Record numbers of women are having babies in their late thirties and forties. The average age of mothers at childbirth is now at its highest: 28.1 years.

The older mum is out there. She has her work. She has a life. And she has a baby or two. The majority of women manage to achieve this without feeling the need for a thrilling fanfare. Not so the older woman for whom time is less gentle.

Some have their children later in life by choice, some by circumstance. Some women have a plan, others get there serendipitously, or by plain mistake. Some are or were in long relationships, some not. Some have concerns about fertility, some fall pregnant in the blink of an eye. There may be compromises in relationships where a father – any father – will do. Or, Mr Right magically appears just as midnight begins to strike on the biological clock. For some of those who do meet Mr Right, the drama commences when they try to persuade him to part with his sperm in a manner that will lead to conception.

One of the great pleasures of writing this book has been the chance to talk to so many women about themselves and their children. For some, their journey may have begun in their twenties. For others it only kicked off in their forties. But the fabric of their lives has a rich and complex texture. To do justice to these women, and to understand how, why and when older motherhood comes about, we need to listen to the intricacies and allow those stories to unfold.

There are three sections to this book, which I've dubbed First, Second and Third Trimester to identify them for easy scanning. The first section is an overview of older mothers' successful pregnancies – both natural and assisted – and failed ones, as well as a discussion of how older women are viewed both medically and by society. The second section is made up entirely of older mothers talking about their lives, and the last section contains medical digests and general interest material on preconceptual care, nutrition, prenatal screening, diagnostic testing and other in-depth medical concerns. So this is a book that can be read as an anthology as well as an informational guide: something to be dipped into for plain facts and practical guidance, or perhaps for a brief, quiet moment of inspiration or comfort.

Though it is designed to be a positive contribution to the debate about older mothers, there are undoubtedly pressing questions to be answered. There are tough aspects to bearing and rearing children, particularly when one is an older mother, and I don't duck them. I've spoken to many experts and quoted some, but where issues are particularly contentious I have, more often than not, given that subject expression through the voices of the mothers themselves. Embedded in their stories are the hard facts, the relevant figures and the daily experiences which, when taken as a whole, describe the lot of the older mother today.

It is impossible for me to write an unbiased, even-handed account of what being an older mother is all about when I feel so completely partisan about the whole thing. Late converts are often the ones who beat the drums and bang the gongs the loudest. Yet I'm not suggesting that the joys of motherhood are necessarily more intense for coming later, rather than earlier. Neither am I saying that the older mother, and her baby, have in some way better experiences than other mothers and babies. What I do say is that an older mother can have an experience of childbearing and rearing that differs very much from the one she would have had when younger. And it is exactly that difference that we'll be exploring in this book.

ENTER CHAOS

The encompassing love a mother has for her child is central to human life. Mothers of all ages speak of their surprise at the intensity and the depth of the passion that they feel for their newborn babies. For many women, these secret love affairs are the sweeter for coming later in life, and the experience becomes a voyage of unexpected pleasure.

Romance and sensuality aside, of course, babies are hard work. They change your life. They prevent you from sleeping. They devastate the body beautiful and bring chaos in their wake. For reasons such as these the job of mothering has become a casualty in the battle for equality.

Yet again and again women take this great leap of faith. As we have seen, more and more older women are doing so, even though some would say they have more to lose than others. A comfortable lifestyle. An established career. A world that is ordered and fashioned to satisfy every personal whim and fancy.

For most older mothers, the physical, emotional and material changes that they must undergo are nothing short of a seismic shift. Patterns, habits and expectations are all the more ingrained simply for having had longer to become established. We hear single people who are older and set in their ways worrying about whether to marry or settle down with someone because they say they have become too 'selfish'. Yet settling into a new relationship with an adult is a piece of cake compared to the effect a newborn baby has on a well-ordered adult life. The intimacy demanded by an infant and its endless needs obliterate time-honoured routines and perfectly honed lifestyles at a stroke.

Conscious of how hard they have worked to get where

they are, older mothers are often more alert than most to what they are giving up. Gone is much of their personal freedom. But gone too, for some of them, is the burden of an existence confused with half-lived longings and no direct investment in the future. It can be an exhilarating challenge, having their world turned upside down and inside out, and knowing that when most of their friends and contemporaries are beginning to prepare for their broods to start leaving the nest, they have only just begun.

We live in a time when women can control their fertility more effectively than at any point in history. And we also live in a time when more and more women are choosing to have their children later than ever. Given those two facts, we have to assume that for those who do have families when older than most, it is through choice.

Most babies are wanted. But late babies – usually planned, often longed for, and thought about for years – are especially wanted. If there have been problems with fertility, these babies may be born against all odds, after long and exhausting fertility treatments.

There is something particularly poignant about the love for a child born late in life. One feels so lucky. The biological clock has been beaten – just.

BEATING TIME: SEX AND SCIENCE

For the older woman who wants a baby, life can rush by at an alarming rate. Incomprehensibly, the biological clock seems to pick up speed. Very suddenly, time is of the essence. She will begin to count off her life in months, or, more precisely, in ovulations. Ovulations come, on average, every 28 days. So, while the rest of the world works to the universally recognised calendar of days, weeks, months, years, all that ends for the older woman who hopes for a child. She must rearrange her timescale by dividing her life into strange segments of 28 days – or 25, or 32, depending on the normal length of her menstrual cycle.

These slabs of time are private and secret. Slices of life that are as removed from other people's experience as the sun is from the moon. Indeed, the woman concerned can herself begin to seem removed and disjointed. That is because her mood swings, her highs and lows, will coincide precisely with her hope at the beginning of a cycle, her elation when she thinks 'it' has worked, and her despair when evidence emerges to the contrary.

Most critically, she has a sense of being hermetically sealed in this private timeframe. The cycles have a beginning and ending that, for her and her only, resonate with a giant thud through the body. They begin when she ovulates. They have a middle, when her next period begins and she realises she is not pregnant, and then they simultaneously end and begin again, as the cycle resumes at the next ovulation.

This is not a subject for dinner party conversation. It is hard to talk over the hors d'oeuvres about the exact temperature one was that morning and the consistency of one's vaginal discharge – both indicators of the state of fertility. But it is likely that these particulars are what our older woman will be thinking about.

She will also be thinking of all the things that help conception. She may make love earlier in the cycle, not at the time of suspected ovulation itself, because there can be surprises and ovulation can often come sooner than you'd think. She will be fine-tuning her sex life so as not to make love too many times. That can make the sperm more dilute and it then spreads too thinly. But, at the same time, to be effective she will want to have sex often enough to get the right chance at the right time.

In an odd reversal after years of sensible contraceptive advice, she will put the diaphragm in *after* making love in order to keep the sperm *in*. That is because, quite often, she's busy, busy, busy and rushing, rushing, rushing and if she's just made love in the morning she'll be dashing to work, and losing the sperm in the process. What chance then for the poor little heroes of making it upwards, when gravity is pulling them downwards?

If she does have time, she will stay in bed with a pillow under her hips, tilting her pelvis backwards so that the sperm stays within. She may in the process also be burning the supper, dying for a pee, missing phone calls, getting behind with the laundry or the PhD thesis . . . But, come what may, she will grit her teeth and lie there unmoving. Because *this* may be *that* time, the only time, the last chance.

Many women of all ages go through these hoops when trying to get pregnant. But for the woman who is running against the clock there can be a desperate edge to the enterprise. How many ovulations has she left before they stop altogether? How close to menopause is she?

Will the fusion happen this time? Will it all come together? Will the magic wand and the fairy godmother and the prince and the gold dust somehow unite into the symphony of creativity that miraculously brings a life into being. Will our older mother-to-be get lucky? Will she go to the ball? Or will she be left with her tattered and ragged hopes scattered in the dust at her feet?

FIRST
TRIMESTER

This section explores older motherhood by looking at it from the inside, in Chapter 1; and then, in Chapters 2 and 3, from the viewpoints of the medicos and the sociologists. Through this inside-out/outside-in approach, we touch on every aspect of older motherhood, from the emotions it awakens to the debates on morality it seems to be sparking off.

CHAPTER 1

The Big Gamble

I suppose one of the things that captures my imagination about older women having children is that it is all about beating the odds and turning convention on its head. An Argentinian woman called Maria Aparacida Brito did nothing, if not that. She gave birth to her eighth child on her sixtieth birthday (yes, that is six-oh). It was a natural delivery with no complications.

Maria started her family later in life than most. Her first boy was born when she was 41, and over the next 16 years she had four boys and two girls. Her doctors were, apparently, mystified – startled that not only did she have her first child so late, but that he was followed by a whole series of natural childbirths.

Her husband Arnaldo though had taken it in his stride, giving a matter-of-fact shrug when asked by the media how the last pregnancy had gone. 'She went to the doctor a few times for prenatal check-ups, and that's it,' he said. 'Hey, she was out there working on the ranch up until the eighth month and there were no problems.' Maria Aparacida has never taken fertility drugs or special medications. Itayene, as she has called her youngest baby, is going to be her last child. Her story is one of the most remarkable I've come across in the realm of older motherhood.

Few of the older women who succeed in becoming mothers have stories as dramatic as Maria Aparacida's. For some, the process is straightforward, with conception, pregnancy, childbirth and childrearing all happening easily and at a time when they were ready. One such story is Andrea Moon's, below.

For other women though, fate is not so kind and their tales, while ultimately positive, attest to how convoluted the road to older motherhood can become, littered with financial difficulties and troubled relationships. There are the older mothers whose problems in conceiving made their route to childbirth, via fertility treatment, an exhausting rollercoaster of hope and despair. Finally, there are the women who have reached a dead end and have had to reconcile themselves to childlessness.

In this chapter we look at the experiences – high, low, long-drawn-out – of older women who have taken their chances with having children. These are only a sampler, designed to show a representative range of the tales they have to tell. Later on, in the second section of this book, we will be looking at a much more comprehensive array of stories, which show how rich and dynamic is the world of these intrepid gamblers.

HAPPY ENDING

Andrea Moon: Mother

'I married late [at 43], having had a very happy and satisfactory career as a psychiatric nurse. I'd always wanted children but, having reached my forties, had resigned myself to enjoying other people's but having none of my own. We didn't deliberately set out to 'have a baby', as my observation of couples who take this route is that they're often not successful. We fell in love and enjoyed lovemaking, and the happy result was that I became pregnant.

Having a first child at this stage of my life was the best thing that could possibly have happened. I'd achieved what I wanted in my career. I was ready for a change and ready to devote myself to my home and baby. I just felt so lucky that that is how it worked out for me. I'd expected a lot of raised eyebrows from the health professionals and friends about such a late pregnancy. I'm a healthy woman and have taken care of myself, and maybe that helped. Maybe I live in an enlightened area: I met a couple of women, pregnant at 30, who were looked upon as elderly by medical staff in two different London hospitals! Maybe the obvious delight of my husband Roger and myself at my pregnant state made people accept it without query.

Whatever the reason, no one turned a hair at my age. Our GP was almost as pleased as we were; my community midwife treated me like any other mum-to-be and a registrar who saw me near the end of the pregnancy at a hospital antenatal appointment suggested a second pregnancy would be most acceptable. No one involved with my care at any stage of the pregnancy or labour seemed to take any notice of my age, and people are now asking me if I'm going to have another child. All very refreshing.

Apart from a small false-alarm bleed early in the pregnancy (too much energetic gardening was the cause, I suspect), it was a very straightforward pregnancy. I had an amniocentesis, because of my age, and waiting for the result of that wasn't a nice experience. I got heartburn, and I got tired as I worked full-time up until two months prior to the birth, but I don't think I fared any worse than younger women and seemed in a rather better state than some I came across. Wanting the baby so much and having an extremely supportive partner no doubt made my life easier than it might be for some younger women.

The only time my age was mentioned was when I asked my GP for a domino birth [standing for 'domiciliary in and out', a scheme involving minimal medical intervention and a short hospital stay]. My midwife was as keen as we were but we couldn't persuade my GP – he was very gentle about not sanctioning and it didn't become a great issue. My midwife told us to wait until the last possible moment before going to hospital and she would come out to me even if she was off duty!

As it happened, my waters broke and so I had to go in. It was a very long, exhausting labour but the end result was the most beautiful eight-and-a-half-pound boy. Maybe I got more exhausted because of my age, but I think it had more to do with being in hospital rather than at home so that I was focused on the pain rather than being distracted by domestic things, and by the fact that baby Rupert had a large head and was slow to move down. It was painful and exhausting and I needed much more help than I'd intended having, but once he was born that fell away as if it hadn't happened.

Rupert is now nearly 15 months old and I have enjoyed every stage of his young life. Maybe if I was younger the broken nights would have been less tiring but I never liked night duty even when I was young! Maybe Rupert will suffer later for having elderly parents, but all I can see at the moment is a positive experience.

I want to be at home with Rupert, watching him grow and develop. I don't resent being tied to the house and not having the freedom to go out in the evenings. I've done a lot of that and the time will come when I can do it again. Comparing how I feel with the younger mums in the postnatal group I seem much happier and more content.

I have a happy lively baby. He has not been difficult, and I'm sure it's because he's come into a peaceful household with parents who have time for him. He's still being breastfed, and he's a very healthy little boy.

There are no rules in my book. For some, having a child early in life is best. For me, being an ancient mum – 44 – is infinitely preferable. Maybe there are some drawbacks, but I haven't found them; and the unexpected bonus of my little one's arrival has brought untold joy to the whole family.

Andrea Moon's experience is not unusual. But for many women it must seem unreal in its calm and ordered progression. Their routes to older motherhood were far less straightforward.

LONG AND WINDING ROADS

With numbers of older mums on the up and up, quite a few women in the public eye have joined this very special club. Their reasons are as varied as one would expect, but one of the more prevalent is that they've entered new relationships.

Perhaps one of the most poignant of these stories is Elizabeth Johnson's. Previously known to the nation as Elizabeth Blakelock, her first husband, PC Keith Blakelock, was hacked to death in the riots on Broadwater Farm, Tottenham, over a decade ago. Elizabeth Blakelock was left to bring up three boys on her own, while trying to shield them from the horrors of their father's death.

She returned to her home in the northeast and began to build a new life, which eventually came to include a new husband, David Johnson. After they married, they thought very long and hard about whether to have a child. There were implications for their immediate family and they didn't take the decision lightly. Then they came to the realisation that there comes a time in your life when you just have to forge ahead and do something for yourself. They decided to go for it.

At the age of 44 Elizabeth Johnson gave birth to their son, Jordan David. She calls him her gift from God. Everyone knows how much they all respect her first husband's memory, what he did and what he was. That will never alter, she says. But that is another life. She hopes that everything goes well for this baby, and that he never has to go through what her first three boys have.

The redemptive, healing quality of new life is a theme that emerges again and again for the older mother. In the case of Elizabeth Blakelock it is a powerful affirmation. Living through the nightmare she did, to then set her face to the future and create a family and home full of hope and love is a testament to incredible bravery.

Having a child may for some be a way of cementing a new relationship, as if a child will give ballast and depth to what might otherwise remain a flimsy vessel. Sometimes this works; sometimes it doesn't. But perhaps, if there are children from an earlier marriage or relationship, some lessons may have been learnt about childrearing, to enrich the now older mother's renewed experience.

The actress Jane Seymour, for example, is 45 and just on the verge of older motherhood. Married for the fourth time two years ago, in a case of hope definitely winning over experience, she is now absolutely thrilled that she is to be a mother again. The actress already has two children: Katie (13) and Sean (9). Her new husband, director James Keach, had secretly hoped that one day they'd have children of their own. When told she was expecting twins she said that she was in a state of complete shock. She was so happy she cried. And when she told James he cried too. Jane has said, 'I have it all now – two great kids, the best role on TV [as the lead in *Dr Quinn, Medicine Woman*] and a husband who's my knight in shining armour. This is the icing on the cake.'

Such perfect timing doesn't, however, always happen. Many who wait for the 'right' time to have a child will never find the opportunity – not least the older parents whose final fertile years are slipping away at great speed. The television newsreader Nicholas Witchell, 42, and his new partner Carolyn Stephenson, also 42, found themselves in a state of relatively bad timing. They have just had their first child, but were in a dilemma over two competing careers. The older parent has had more years to invest in a career, and so has more to lose when baby and partner pull in different directions.

Though delighted with the arrival of daughter Arabella, Nicholas and Carolyn had to make some pretty quick decisions. Nicholas Witchell has worked for the BBC for 20 years, initially covering the trouble spots of the world and latterly working on the early morning news programme.

17

A confirmed bachelor, he had been about to leave for Jerusalem to become the BBC's Middle East correspondent, a job he had wanted for a long time, when he met Carolyn and his life underwent a radical shift. For her part, Carolyn had a thriving, 17-year-old jewellery design business with a devoted clientele.

The baby's arrival therefore focused their minds, and they began realigning their priorities immediately. Says Nick, 'Babies are always precious, but they are even more precious when you are 40. You have lived life a little bit. Perhaps you feel you can give a little more to being a parent.' Certainly, he seems to be prepared to give up Jerusalem for now.

In an apparent contradiction, the arrival of a baby may, for some women, be the moment they choose to focus on their career. With her domestic life 'sorted out', she feels there is now time to pick up the threads again. That is what one actress who starred in a James Bond film has done.

At the age of 44, she has had a second daughter and now, with the baby just toddling, feels that she is 'free at last' to resume her career. 'My career's been more or less on hold since the arrival of my first daughter. I wanted to be a proper mother to her, and I wanted to have another baby. I knew I wouldn't feel totally at one with myself until I'd had the children I dreamed of having. But now I feel able to get back into the marketplace and pursue my career in the sort of unhindered way that I was never able to do before. Having my second and last child means that's it, full stop. Now it's time to kickstart my career.'

Older motherhood certainly hasn't cramped this actress's style. Indeed, she seems to be calmly in control of the direction in which she is going, and making determined moves to get there. But other women have felt considerably hindered by the emotional baggage that they bring to their role of older mother. For some, it lends a degree of objectivity that can help as one negotiates the demands of a new baby. For others the chaos remains chaos and the white noise of emotional turmoil and upheaval continue to make life hard and wearing. There is no guarantee that being an older mother magically confers a benign maturity, or smooths out the more tortuous of life's tangles.

Lorna Jacobs: Management Consultant, Mother

My impression is that mothers of 25 get just as exhausted as older mothers. A mother of 20 can be just as whacked as a mother of 42. And that's because they've said so. My daughter Clare is coming up to four and I'm 44 and she still wakes during the night. Not regularly, but often. When she's away I do my best to catch up. She goes off to school for the after-noon and I have a sleep.

It has been complicated in that I have had four subsequent pregnancies since her birth, each time feeling very sick and very tired, and so she's used to the fact that Mummy goes and lies down. But . . . I think that your levels of exhaustion have much more to do with your own internal dynamism and what's going on in your life and how much stress you've got. How much support you have. I may not have the energy at 44 that I had at 24, but I may still have more energy than another woman does at 24. And, at the age of 44 I've learnt how to prioritise and work out where best to use what energy I do have.

And learn that *I'm* important. I take the time I

need. I mean, there was no ironing done for six months. The house didn't get cleaned. And I think a woman of 25 would not have had the self-confidence to 'indulge' herself in that way. I had been through things. I had ended up in a psychiatric clinic through *not* looking after myself, so you learn.

Being 'older' means you've probably had a lot of life experience to draw on. I've had a lot to handle. I was divorced at 34. Went into the psychiatric clinic when I was 38. Got engaged to my husband about a month before I was 40. On my fortieth birthday I found I was pregnant. Which was an absolute joy. Since then I've had my daughter. And then four miscarriages. Simon's been out of work more times than he's been employed since we married. He's a management consultant. He had a complicated previous relationship which has caused great conflict for us. There were two children from that relation-ship. We've had a two-year court battle. And my mother died a month ago. That's a lot to have coped with. How many people of 25 could have coped with that and surfaced successfully? It makes me much more relaxed about many things.

For instance: my daughter is nearly four and she still doesn't do poo in the toilet. She still has a nappy on. I don't *care*! I know it's not going to last forever. We've been tested sorely by the legal battle that lasted two years but have come out the other end, and I know that my husband and I are still very much together. When *that* can happen it gives you a different perspective. My daughter's not going to be doing poo in her nappy at 18. Things pass.

The first few months she *screamed* and *screamed* and *screamed*, but it isn't for ever. All you can do is love her and hold her and cuddle her for the time being. And give her everything because she's not going to be like that always.

And there are the joyful times. I remember one time when she was about 10 months. She was sitting on the edge of the washbasin and I was trying to hurry a bit because I wanted to get out and do some shopping. The cold tap was dripping and she put her toes under it. And chuckled. And put her toes under it again. And quite clearly this was a new experience. And I can remember quite consciously thinking, 'Damn the shopping. I do shopping day in day out. That will happen again. Her doing this is time to indulge. Enjoy. Because you're not going to get it again.'

It was just wonderful to see her face and to see where the moment led to. We don't know how intelligent she is. She is obviously bright. She has a very extensive vocabulary. People say to us, they don't know how clever she is or how much it is the attention she gets. Every child gets put in front of a video. And she does as well. But what we do is involve her in what we're doing too. So that when I'm making bread she's there making bread with me. When I'm washing up, she's got a little bowl on the floor and is washing up her tea set.

It takes more time. But it's an investment. And I feel very strongly that it is a passage of time that you don't get again.

But my story really starts at my divorce. Everyone seemed to think I coped admirably with my divorce. My sisters say how brave I was. I made sure that it was as amicable as possible. He had met a Czecho-slovakian woman before the Velvet Revolution and

21

she got pregnant. It would have been quite difficult for her to get out. If he'd married her that would have helped. But if the child was born before they were married then there would have been no way of getting the child out. So I had to expedite the divorce so that they could get married, so that child could come out. I kept myself busy and three years later I collapsed.

When I was in the psychiatric clinic they had a session on bereavement and I suddenly realised that I'd never shouted and screamed and done all the angry things you should about divorce. And then the next layer under that was the relationship with my parents.

My father, for a variety of reasons, was away for 10 months a year, every year, until I was 13. Mummy was a teacher and very wrapped up in her work. She would come home absolutely exhausted without any time for her own four children.

After being in the clinic I thought . . . my God, my poor mother. Full-time job with four children growing up. And on her own.

Having seen my parents do that means I am *not* going to *go out to work!* Not full time. For my daughter. I also haven't got a job to go back to. Just after I met Simon I lost my job.

I'd been out of the psychiatric clinic for two years before I met Simon. I'd been in five weeks altogether and was more or less stable by then. I was 38. I talked to a friend of someone whom I had gone out with and he suggested I try 'Executive Leasing', which is sort of management temping. He said he'd get a friend of his who was doing it to give me a ring. And Simon gave me a ring. And I chatted and I thought . . .

mmmm! He sounds rather nice.

I established that he didn't have anyone immediately in his life and said to him that it would be quite good if he was looking for work, as I was, for us to team up. All the books say you should find a buddy to work with. How about we meet? And at some point he realised he was being chatted up and it went from there.

We got engaged in October, and in the November I was pregnant. It took one month. One opportunity. I didn't feel like an older mum. I think that most people who have their family and then what always used to be thought of as 'the afterthought' or 'the mistake', the menopausal baby, don't think of themselves as older mums.

We were both a bit dumbstruck. It was still quite a new relationship. We'd known each other for about 15 months. He'd taken a lot of encouraging to commit himself again.

You sort of say, 'Well, we'll get engaged . . . and then that's not final. You get engaged on the basis that you see how it feels to make that commitment, before moving on to the next stage. But then when you're pregnant you think there's no getting out of this. Then I think I was really very scared. I'm fairly sure that part of being very sick was also part of that. I mean we weren't living together. He was living in Reading and I was living in Guildford. He's Jewish. I have converted since but I hadn't at that time. I suppose a bit of me thought is he just going to run away again? Having in the back of my mind that my father had run away and my first husband had run away. We got married in the February when I was four months pregnant. And it was sort of like trying to find a gap when hopefully I would be feeling less sick, but I wouldn't have got too enormous to wear a wedding dress. And we knew that there were these other two children from his previous relationship. The maintenance for them had got sorted through an unbelievably ghastly court case.

The one thing that he says that attracted him to me was that I was not prepared to play games. Within weeks of meeting him I had said, 'I'm not saying I want to marry you and have your children. But what I am saying is I am coming up to 39. I want to get married and have children. If that is not what you want out of a relationship let's finish it *now*. Because I'm not wasting the next year of my life, which is very precious to me, playing silly games with you.' If you want to have children that is what you have to say by the time you get to the age I was then. That is the drama of the older woman. I don't have time on my side.

So this was the backdrop to our relationship. In order for me to become a mother I had to persuade this man it was not going to be like his first experience of parenthood a second time around.

After the four miscarriages, I don't think we will try again. I think it's going to take me a long time to get over my mother. I need for Simon to have a job. I need to get some reserves back. And then I'll be 45. And then you get into *really* being an old mum. The gap between Clare and the next baby would be five years, so you're not getting the companionship that you want. It would mean starting all over again. All the work things I'm building up . . . in a sense you could retain the contacts. But it would be very much hard work. Trying to get childminders for two children, one who's at school and a baby. . . it all gets so much more complicated. We've been told there's a 50 per cent chance that I'd have another miscarriage. I haven't got the stamina for it.

And the thought of being 60 and having a 15-year-old! The thought of being 60 and having a 20-year-old! Well, at least she'll be off to university or she'll have left home or something. But the thought of turning 60 and having this possibly vile rebellious 15-year-old. You can imagine . . . I find it so funny, these gorgeous girls at 15, they're all in black with their great bovver boots on. I feel at 60 . . . could I really cope with that?

Clare is absolutely beautiful. She is so precious. When I converted to Judaism I had to choose a Jewish name. And I'd chosen one that is like Lorna so that I can recognise it easily. But my other name, the one that has the most meaning for me, is the Jewish word for 'blessed'. And I *feel* blessed. At quite considerable price I have got something beyond price.

THE ABSOLUTELY LAST CHANCE SALOON: BOOSTING FERTILITY

The stories we have just read, however fraught, are all characterised by one thing : the older mothers in question managed to give birth without resorting to fertility drugs or intervention. Many older women aren't as lucky, and it is safe to say that broadly speaking, the fertility business is an industry which has had a direct and dramatic effect on the chances of older women having a child.

The scientific breakthroughs that we've seen in recent years have presented us with a continuous series of new and increasingly improbable permutations on 'normal' procreation. The heated debate about the first 'test-tube' baby, Louise Brown, has long since faded away. But when it was still hot as an issue, there was a definite whiff of sulphur about as experts and pundits warned us of Frankenstein's monsters somehow materialising out of the pipette and presenting us with apparitions too grotesque to contemplate.

One of the latest breakthroughs is the multiple pregnancy delayed over time. 'Meet the astonishing Finney Quads' roars the headline, and indeed they do surprise. There is gloriously bouncing 14-month-old Edward playing peekaboo with Harry, Abigail and Ben, his sister and brothers who are all of five weeks old. All of them are test-tube babies, the product of eggs fertilised at the same time; but the three that were to become Harry, Ben and Abigail were frozen until Mrs Finney was ready to become pregnant again after Edward's birth.

Among the most contentious of the new fertility procedures is the one that facilitates a pregnancy for those who are postmenopausal – those women whose ovaries have stopped producing eggs, who are no longer fertile, who are the other side of menopause. The treatment involves egg donation, which is probably the most likely form of successful treatment for those with absolutely everything stacked against them. And the postmenopausal mother is nothing if not that.

She is, most obviously, amongst the oldest of older mothers. One of the main things going against her is people's attitudes. Almost without exception, the medical experts I spoke to about this new permutation of 'egg-meets-sperm-meets-habitable-venue-for-generating-life' were against it – except, of course, those carrying out the operation. And the mothers themselves.

Pauline Lyon: Mother

It started for us in January 1993. That's when we first went to the BUPA hospital in Norwich because they were advertising a special offer on IVF [*in vitro* fertilisation, where the egg is fertilised in a test tube] treatment. A bit cheaper than normal. We went along there and they said they'd accept us onto the books. And we went along a fortnight later and they'd done some tests . . . David's sperm was all right. But I found out I'd used up all my eggs. And they didn't do egg donation there then. So they said the only thing for me would be egg donation, and they referred me to the Lister Hospital in London.

I'm a postmenopausal mother. I was having regular periods, that was the thing. I never realised you only had so many eggs. And I don't think a lot of other people realise that either. I was totally shocked. I came out crying. They said go away and think about egg donation. One minute you're thinking you're going to have one naturally and then the next minute you're told you're not. Unless you're somebody who desperately wants a baby it's hard to explain. Your world falls apart for that moment, till you're offered another option.

We had joined a fertility group in Norwich previously and we used to go along there once a month. Naturally I was the oldest one there. All the others were young, in their twenties and suchlike. But we were all in the same position. All trying for babies. All different things going wrong. And each month there were just a certain amount of people who could bring themselves to talk about their problem.

David and I used to talk about it. All the treatments and that. Unless you're on a treatment nobody can understand the stress, and what that causes. A lot of the young people said their families think you pay your money, you go up, and you have your baby. But it's not like that. There's all the in-between part. It's very stressful. One minute you're up. Next minute you're down.

My first marriage broke up when my daughter was six. And I had two other relationships, but none I'd want a family with. But when I met David that was different. I was 47 when we met. And I thought, this is a man I want to have a child with. We both wanted a child. He's a year younger than me. I've always loved babies and he felt the same way. We felt it would seal the marriage.

We both had grown-up children, but that's not the same as having your own together. Though people say our daughter is more David's. And they ask, does she feel mine. And she does feel mine because that's my blood supply that kept her alive, the same as it did my daughter, 24 years ago. But I suppose people find that hard to understand as well.

I could never accept that I would never have another baby. I used to think oooooooooooh . . . maybe one day I will. I just couldn't get it into my brain that I wouldn't. Which really is the way you've got to be. If you think everything's going to go wrong all the while well then, things *do* go wrong.

When we first went to the Lister they said we'd have to go on a waiting list for a donor and they give you posters to put up. And they give you a reference number and they put that on the poster. Then if anyone rings up the hospital they say your reference number and that automatically puts you to the top of the list. You don't get their eggs. But you get somebody else's. If you can get your own donor you jump the queue.

We put the posters in doctor's offices, libraries, anywhere we could think of. We gave them to relations to put up in different parts of the country. David's family live down in Sussex, so we sent them all down there. And I used to put an advert in the local free paper every week for an egg donor. I used to keep changing it to try and make it sound a bit better. I've put them in my scrapbook. I used to put, 'Urgently wanted. Lady egg donor. Aged between 19 to 35 years old' – that's the age they used to say at the hospital – 'for an infertile couple. Time is running out due to early menopause.'

They don't really tell you at the Lister who's responded. What happens often is that once the people ring up and find out that in order to be donors they have to take all the same drugs as us, that puts people off. And they have to keep travelling to London as well. That's hard, isn't it? Egg donation is such a new thing.

It's really hard to find egg donors. At one time David's niece was going to donate. She's got two children. But once she knew she had to take all the drugs, that chucked her off. We still don't know where we got the donation from. They don't tell the donors either. They try and match you up as best you can with eye colour, hair colour, height and that sort of thing.

I was over the moon that I could try for a child. But then they tell you how many's on the waiting list, and you think, 'God, will I ever get a turn?' In the end, we had to wait just over 12 months. It was awful. Horrible. But I never gave up hope. Some people wait longer. There's a two- to three-year waiting list.

Then one day, out of the blue, they suddenly phoned me and said they'd got a donor. I couldn't believe it. One minute they tell you you're that far down on the list. That's why I wonder if we did get any follow-up to the advert . . .

I was on hormone injections to build up the womb so that it was ready to accept the eggs. The lining of the womb has to be a certain thickness before they will put the eggs in. They make an appointment when you'll both be in the hospital on the same day. Our donor was on drugs to help her produce eggs, but on the day we were called to the hospital she hadn't produced any.

We got all the way up to London. She went in the morning and we went in the afternoon – that's so you don't meet – and of course she hadn't produced any. So we were all upset again. Especially all the way to London with all that erratic driving through London. Then, when we had to drive all the way back to Norwich, I was crying all the way. That was such a big disappointment.

People don't understand. It's unbearable. I thought that was the only chance I'd get and I wondered if I'd get another one. But then they did phone up with another donor within about a month. And that time David's sperm didn't fertilise the eggs. And we had to pay for that. We hadn't had to pay for the one who didn't produce eggs but we had to pay for the second one because it was more or less our fault. Even so. Another drive back crying.

So then they phoned up with another. And this

time she produced 13 eggs, 7 of them fertilised. And the doctor said to me (I was on the table, and he was ready to put the eggs inside me), 'How do you feel about having triplets?' 'Triplets!' I went. 'They're such good embryos I really daren't put three in,' he said. If they'd all taken he would have had to have taken one away. He wouldn't want to risk my health with three. Twins would have been bad enough. So he only put two in.

Then a fortnight later you go back and do a blood test and when we went back we found they hadn't. They had put 2 in, out of the 7 fertilised, so that left 5 left from before. Which they froze. When they thawed them out for our next attempt only three survived. So that was two more gone. The doctor was so embarrassed when I went back. He said he wished he'd put all three in the first time. So he put the last three in. And one took!

I was 49 when I conceived. But I said I was 47. And I didn't half mind telling them the wrong age. And the consultant had a chat with us and we didn't know what the cut-off age was. We just filled in the form. He said to David, 'I advise you to go and knock two years off Pauline's age.' I said, 'Ooooh no. I can't do that. I'm not the type of person to lie.' And the consultant said, 'I'm afraid if you want to have one attempt that's what you'll have to do.' So David went and changed the form.

So. We were due to go to the Lister on the Friday for the test but I just didn't want to wait. I thought I'd go and get a pregnancy kit. Then of course, when the line came up, I couldn't believe it. I thought, 'Oh no. That must be a dud test.' David was so worried (he was starting a new job), I thought I daren't tell him.

If I ring and tell him he'll want to come home. I kept that to myself from the Tuesday to the Friday. Never told anybody at all.

When we got to the Lister we only sat there 25 minutes. The nurse came through and I looked at her face and she wasn't smiling or anything. And we went in this little room and she said, 'Oh! I don't know how to contain myself. It's positive.' And we all stood there howling. The three of us. Just couldn't believe it.

Then I started panicking because you have to take the drugs for so long to build the lining of the womb up. And your progesterone has to be a certain level before you can stop the drugs. And I thought the minute I stop taking it I'll lose the baby, because there's a higher risk of miscarriage with egg donation. But luckily everything went all right and I never had any blood loss at all. The whole way through. I was fit as a fiddle.

And at the Lister Hospital when we first went they were doing this research on the density of bones in older women, and they asked me to take part. The doctor said at the beginning, before I was pregnant, that my density was above normal to start with. You go back when the baby's six weeks old, and mine is even higher now. He said having a baby has done me *good*. The bones were good to start with but all the calcium flowing about through the pregnancy has made them even better. So that's another myth out the window,

The birth was a piece of cake. Well, I had a Caesarean, didn't I? The obstetrician said he wanted to do me at 38 weeks: he didn't want to take a chance of my going into labour because they'd never dealt with anyone as old as me having a baby. And they don't know how your body's going to react. But my blood pressure was high, and my legs were swelling up. It was creeping up above my knee and I was getting a bit worried. When they decided to go ahead with it I was over the moon.

They were all laughing. The anaesthetist had to come and check me out before and he wanted to know if I had any false teeth . . . !!! And I said David had never seen me *without* my false teeth! It had to be a general anaesthetic because with egg donation sometimes the placenta doesn't know when to stop growing. Because of the drugs to encourage the womb to grow in preparation for the baby, the placenta sometimes starts growing into the lining of your womb, and they have to do a hysterectomy as well. In no time at all it was all over and I was coming round and I could hear them trying to wake me up. And all I could think was that my stomach hurt. I thought I was dying then. And I could hear David running around saying, 'Ooooohhhhh!!! It's a *girl*. It's a *girl!* That's *perfect*. There's nothing the matter with her.'

The pain was so bad that night I thought I was dying. But it was all forgotten the next morning. And now, seven weeks later, there's no pain. They kept saying they couldn't believe how well I'd got over it. And I couldn't believe it either. When I actually was fully conscious and saw her, I was over the moon. You can't take your eyes off her.

My older daughter's all right now. She was a bit funny to begin with. It's still just David's two daughters don't want anything to do with us. But we've got our baby. And we're full of energy. And I would say to any woman who's postmenopausal and wants a baby to go for it. They must never give up hope. Whatever age you are. I know it costs a lot of money because you can't get it on the NHS. We had to get a loan out on the mortgage. But it's all well worth it in the end. You can never put a price on it. And you can never thank the donors enough.

Pauline Lyon's state-of-the-art pregnancy and childbirth happened because she'd found someone she really loved – and never mind the fact that she was in her late forties. Jackie Barrett's story is perhaps a far more common one: that of a successful career woman in her late thirties who suddenly finds she can't conceive. Her experience is a testament to life with IVF treatment.

Jackie Barrett: Managing Director, Mother

I'd been with Greg, not married, but together 10 years and we were living in the States. I was around 33 when we went there, and two years later the old biological clock seemed to come to a stop and say, OK, your time is up. Now is the time to have a baby.

I went off the Pill and then spent two years without any success. I wasn't maniacally stressed by it, but just very aware nothing was happening. We both work, and I was working very hard and being very successful at the time. (I run a film production company producing television commercials.)

We came back to the UK partly because of the baby thing. And to set up an office here. But the baby issue was very much on my mind, though not at the forefront. It was beginning to be a stress point between us after a year or two. It is then that you start thinking, maybe we're not doing it enough. Maybe Greg has a problem. Maybe I have the problem.

I always had a secret suspicion I had a problem because I did suffer from PID [pelvic inflammatory disease] when I was about 25. I got it from having the coil. I knew I had had it. What I didn't know was what damage it does, and did. My Fallopian tubes were really badly affected. One was completely withered away and the other one completely blocked. I was given a huge antibiotic treatment at the time to get rid of it.

I don't think I was told and I feel very angry about it. But then fate has a hand in one's life. Maybe if I'd known at 26 I couldn't conceive children my life would have been totally different. Maybe I wouldn't have gone into the relationship that I did, if I didn't think I could give Greg children ... Anyway, once back, we started going to doctors. I didn't do it on the NHS, for the simple reason of my age, and time. By now I was 37.

My GP is a man whose father brought me into the world. I've known him all my life and he's very easy to talk to. So they tested us out and they decided to do a laparoscopy. And then I was told that I couldn't conceive children.

I was completely shocked. All my life my assumption was I was going to have children. My mother said to me, 'Well, darling, you made your choice. You went into a career,' and I said 'No! I did *not* make the choice. Because at that stage it never was a choice. I was going to have children. And I was going to have my career.' I was sobbing. I was horrified. I couldn't talk to anyone. Everything went through my mind. That Greg would leave me. That I was going to be a spinster with no children.

But I'm an 'up' and positive person. I then called back the doctor, once I'd calmed down. I said, 'Right. I want to know what my options are. What I can do. What I can't do.' I was told basically that I had the option of surgery. That the best man to go to was Robert Winston at the Hammersmith. That he is NHS and it would be a couple of years possibly before I got an operation. My other option would be to go for IVF. And the doctor told me the percentage that the IVF clinics were giving out then was a 25 per cent success rate. In fact, I found out that the true percentage success figure of live births at that time was 9 per cent. They have a lot of pregnancies that become ectopic. And a lot of their pregnancies, *then*, used to miscarry. We're talking about 1987.

Both Greg and I work and though we're not wealthy, we're comfortable. And therefore I had the money that it takes to go for IVF. I decided to go to the Hallam Clinic off Harley Street, which at that time was affiliated with the Bourne Clinic up in Cambridge where IVF had been pioneered. I did four attempts. Very stressful. You're very keyed up when you go. You go and sit in a waiting room full of tension. Because in that waiting room are couples who have got *no* chance at all. Couples who are possibly pregnant and are waiting for their results. Couples who know they've got a problem, but don't know what it is. There's the odd mother who's got her first child with her. Which is very, very hard. But why shouldn't they bring their babies with them? And there are pictures on the walls of babies produced through the clinic. You can't run away from it. But the people at the clinic, the doctors and the nurses and everyone involved, are absolutely *wonderful*.

When you get your bad result, everybody takes it differently. Once I sobbed. Once I didn't react at all and just walked out. Once I charged out in anger. I did get to the stage where I had to stop seeing my friends with babies. In fact we went to a fireworks night with some great friends of mine. They had two children of their own and we joined them and I felt weird. I just had to get away. I realise, in retrospect, I shut myself off. It was the only way to handle the pain.

All I can say is that when I *was* pregnant . . . you can see it in my face. I was looking at some old pictures the other day, and you can see that I was the happiest I've ever been in my whole life. And it was that sense of completion, of doing everything that you're on this earth to do.

While you're having IVF, before you get pregnant, *if* you get pregnant, you have to spend a lot of time thinking that you are going to have to come to terms with living the rest of your life without children. And it is the most ghastly, ghastly thing. It was grief. I used to sob. The positive side for me was that I was doing everything within my power to get pregnant. So that helped me mentally. The worst stress time is when you go in to have the eggs taken out. The first time I had it done I did pass out with the pain. From the second time onwards they did it a different way, which was new at the time and brilliant. Some people don't actually produce any eggs. I was incredibly fertile, and produced something like 23 eggs the first time.

So then they put it with the sperm and that goes

into the dish. And then two days later they tell you whether it's fertilised and how many they've got to put back. You're on call, really. So you go in and have them put back, which is completely painless, but very nervewracking. And then there's two weeks of deep, deep stress. Every time you go to the loo you're looking for your period. But I resolved to carry on until I got pregnant or until the money ran out. Whichever came first. God knows if I'd had to go six, seven, eight times . . .

I nearly passed out when they told me the final attempt had worked. But afterwards I skipped down the street. Greg happened to be in New York and I just got straight on the phone and called him and said, 'We're pregnant.' I was overjoyed. Greg was over the moon too. And I loved every second of it. I had a fabulous pregnancy. I was completely healthy the whole way through. I swam the whole way through. I had given up caffeine and smoking as soon as I started thinking about becoming pregnant.

Meeting the baby when he was born, was just to die for. He was divine. He was a very good baby. I was very lucky I had a baby that slept through the night. He was a dream baby actually. Fed brilliantly. Weaned him onto the bottle brilliantly. He was the perfect bub. A joy.

For the second one – I went through the whole thing again. We did, very early, rather stupidly, but understandably, when Freddie was three months, we looked at each other and we were having such joy with him, that we said, 'Let's start again.' Knowing that we had to go through the test tube again. And I went for my first treatment again, at four months after Freddie's birth. We were on a complete high. I had been since the birth. When they saw me coming through the door at the IVF clinic they laughed at me. They said I was mad. And it was odd, but the desire for child number two was different, but almost as strong as the desire for number one. I was determined he wasn't going to be an only child. I was as determined. But I didn't have the stress in the same way.

I was terribly, terribly lucky. Having children has brought total fulfilment to my life. It gives you an extraordinary confidence. That I had never realised before. As an individual. I have confidence in my life now and all facets of my life that I didn't have before I had children. And a great happiness. It opens up another side that you don't know exists. Observations that you've forgotten about. You see things differently.

I'd tell anyone to go for it. At whatever age. My GP was the one who started this. I thought I was too old. '*Absolutely* not,' he said. 'I've just had a patient, 48, who's just had a baby. *Go for it.*' And my obstetrician was the same.

I quite enjoy being an older mum. I like all that side of it. And I think, 'Gosh, I don't want to go out clubbing and all of that. I'm really happy to be at home with the children, when I am, and have their routine. I love it. It makes me feel younger.'

For some women the pleasure of a late baby was not so much the baby itself but the new person who came into her life and made it complete. One such woman is Gill Grant who gains increasing joy from her son as he grows up.

Gill Grant: Freelance Television Producer/Journalist, Mother

I had a home birth, and I had to write a letter disclaiming any responsibility, sign it and give it to my GP. She wouldn't let me have a home birth as I was 38 and they don't allow anyone over 35 to have them in this area. You're too elderly! Fortunately it went well and things were very straightforward.

But those are small details compared to what happens after the birth. The bringing up of the child itself. The most obvious feature for me of being an older mother was the discrepancy in age between what he was, and what I thought he should be. When I had Paul, I thought he should arrive fully formed and eight years old!

I remember when he was eight months, I kept on saying to him, 'Why aren't you *eight*! You should be bringing home homework by now. What are doing being a baby?' And I've never ever got over that. I've got this figure eight stuck in my head for some reason. I feel that I should have had a baby at no later than 30.

So now, when I am 48, he should be at university! The offshoot of that is that I've always treated him as roughly eight years older than he is. I have very adult conversations with him. I let him watch grown-up programmes till way beyond the nine o'clock threshold. We discuss things that really perhaps children shouldn't be discussing . . . like where can we get the best interest rate on our return. That sort of thing. And because I treat him like that, all the teachers at his school say they cannot believe that Paul is only nine.

I let him swear, because adults do and I can't see why I should stop him. I don't bat an eyelid. When he was a baby I never did baby talk with him. He's so dependent, really. Obviously babies and toddlers and little children are dependent on their mothers if they're an only child and you haven't got help. I've always wanted him to be more independent. So he says, 'Mummy, you've got to take me to school tomorrow,' and I say 'Catch the blooming bus! What's wrong with the Number 46.' And then you get replies that make you realise they're very little. 'I don't know where the bus stop is.'

We were passing through Oxford to see friends and I thought I'd just show him the Oxford University colleges. And he said, 'Mummy, these look like haunted old castles. I don't want to go here.' And of course I don't want that babyish response. I want him to say, 'Yes, I think I'll go to Balliol.' Then you realise you've turned him off university for life. So. The discrepancy I've never got over, and never will get over. Until he's grown up. And I can see he's just beginning to overtake me in some areas now, like I can't do his maths and his computing is absolutely brilliant. I look forward to the time when that switchover happens.

Also, if you have a baby late and you think, 'My God, I've finally done it!' you are less likely to have a second child. You think this is too much like hard work. The number of times I've said that. It *is* hard work. The thought of having two of them was actually horrendous. As much as you love your child and you would never be without him, and I preface all of this by saying he is by far the most creative and productive and wonderful thing that I have ever done in my whole life . . . *but* . . . on the other hand there are just times when I long to put my feet up.

They're *so* much work when they're babies. I had an easy birth, it wasn't that that put me off. It was the work afterwards, and trying to combine it with my own work, which is impossible. You just think blow this for a lark, I'm not going through this again. There was a time when Paul wanted a little sister. I couldn't tell him the honest truth. So I said I was too old.

I didn't even think about having another one. But the consequence of that is that he wants to play with his Mummy all the time. They need company, and they need a playmate and when they're four years old a woman in her forties is not the best one going. It's a very remarkable woman who's still got the ability to play with gunge and messy paint. And you've reached the stage in your life where you want everything to be really clean, tidy and in order.

But I've seen younger mothers who do relish the *Blue Peter* side of being a mum. Where it is all sloshy paint everywhere, and you've got to make things, cut them up and stick them together and all that. And you'd rather be reading an intelligent novel in a quiet spot at the back of the garden.

Now that he's older and he's got tons of homework and it's all why the Roman army marched 26 miles a day, it's more intellectual stuff, and I can actually key into it.

Yet there's this conflict of always wanting to do *my* thing. He wants to do his thing, which is a million miles away from what I want to do. I will never get over that conflict. This could apply to mothers of any age, but certainly for women who are older, if you have a baby late in life you have got used to doing your own thing and being quite selfish. A child is so demanding. I have never ever got over not having any freedom.

When you are working full time as I am, and you don't have full-time childcare, something has got to give, and the sacrifice has been me. And it's your own health and beauty and appearance that gives. I don't like having to compromise my appearance just to be with my son.

Although I have childcare while I'm working, I walk through the door and she's *out*. I never have time to catch my breath. You're either at work or you're looking after your child in the house. I have a mother's help who comes in between school and the time I get home from work. And I have a separate cleaner. So I don't have to do all the chores.

The other thing is you find yourself eating the food that you make for your child and his little friends. What they want for lunch is frankfurters and chips. Or pizzas. And now I'm ten and a half stone! My partner's work takes him away from home a lot. He travels around the world so I am to all intents and purposes a single mum. When he's here he doesn't help in the house. But he does take Paul around a lot. He's a good chauffeur!

And again when you get to your forties, you quite like your house to be nice. So I bought these nice lampshades and I had all these lovely ornaments that I brought back from my travels in Mexico and places like that, and Paul and his father, depending on the season, they have turned our lounge into a sports arena. So bits of furniture are moved around and turned into wickets, or whatever. The wall is a squash court and he's practising his backhand on that. When it's a football pitch the sofa end is one goal and the chairs the other.

His ninth birthday. I cannot tell you what complete chaos. It was like *Lord of the Flies* come to life. We had 30 nine- or ten-year-olds. They were complete savages. I have to work flat out because he's at private school. I've chosen to send him to an independent school and that's my own choice. The fees are £200 a week. And it's worth it because he's now able to hold intelligent conversations. If he was at a state school I'm not convinced that he would. I want him to go into some kind of highly paid job in the professions so that I don't have to support him. You're starting so late as an older parent. I don't feel I can carry on doing these 10-hour days at work, in my sixties.

But the irony is, though I'm doing it for him, he will say, 'Mum, I never see you. You're coming home too late.' I walk through the door at 8.30pm after a 12-hour shift, and he points to his watch and says '*Muuuum*! What kind of time is this to come home from work? I had to have dinner without you. *Muuuumm*!' And you want to say, I'm doing it just for you, but then you can't because they're going to feel guilty that their mum is grinding herself into the ground for their benefit.

There are only 13 to 18 in his class. They get a lot of individual attention, and I'm working round the clock so that I can pay for his school fees so that he can support himself when I'm old and grey. Which I am now, except I colour it. Because he doesn't want to *see* grey. One day he gasped, 'Aaaaaghh!! You've got grey hair coming through, I can *see* it. It's terrible, Mummy.' You're forced to keep looking younger for the benefit of your young son. And where work is concerned they would prefer that you be there. The greatest gift that they can have is to have their mum with them. Even if she's a boring old fart. They want your company.

I don't have regrets having him. I just wish I was able to better balance it. What I haven't managed to get right, is that we both benefit. He's benefiting at my expense. I have got shelves upon shelves upon shelves of good books. I have one particular 'To Be Read' shelf and it's now expanded onto other shelves. Because I never *ever* can sit down for five minutes and read a good book.

John, my husband, when he's here, is very playful I must say. They get up to all their sports in the sitting room. And he'll sit down and play board games with him for hours. So Paul's biggest playmate is his 65-year-old dad.

I do preface all this negativity by saying that I wouldn't be without him for the world. I realise that in order to have him I am making sacrifices. Not just compromises, but sacrifices. And I do it without a second thought. You just go into motherhood mode. And you don't do it grudgingly.

I remember before I had him there was always this feeling when I was 37 and younger of a sort of void in one's life. A real gap. It's not so much broodiness. But there was a feeling of something terribly important missing in my life. And the minute, the split second the baby was born, that void is filled. It's amazing. It's like a massive jigsaw piece in one's life goes into place.

All those longings of how do I fulfil my life, are just gone. And you suddenly realise this is what it's all about. Everything I do, I do for him.

The up side is, you have a mate for life. And it's an intimate relationship. I do have a very, very close bond with him. Partly because he's a single child and because I treat him like an equal. Both of which are a function of me being an older mother. He tells me things that perhaps a lot of children wouldn't tell their mothers. And, in fact, I compare with other parents and they say they have no idea what's going on in their kids' lives. I hear everything. I even hear who had a paper dart thrown at them. And I get all the dirty jokes, because that's the stage he's at. They are things I would never have told my mother at his age. But he never thinks I'm going to be cross or disgusted by them. Which I may be, but I never say I am. I like the idea of having a child who tells me everything.

I am probably the most liberal mother of the children in Paul's class. I have a perspective that means I've seen more. I think, in the general scheme of things, it doesn't matter if he tells dirty jokes. There are more important things to be concerned about.

And I have to say when I look at him I am so proud. He is everything that a mother could ever want in a son. He is extraordinarily good-looking for a start. Even though I say so myself. I look at him and I think, that boy is *so* gorgeous. He's tall, dark and handsome. He's very, very smart. He's highly intelligent and clever. Charming, talented, the lot. I work in television production, and it pales into insignificance when I look at managing to produce a child like that. So you are prepared to make all the sacrifices.

He's a lovely child. I'm doing a very good job on

him. Every single time I go to the parents and teachers meeting they say he's the kind of child who makes teaching worthwhile and a delight. So what I'm doing, and all of my sacrifices, are worth it. 'What a fine young man he's turning out to be,' they say.

MINDING THE GAP: HANDLING CHILDLESSNESS

For women who want children, to have to come to terms with a life that will not include them can be unbearable, causing immense despair. Carol Drinkwater, the actress who made her name as Helen Herriot in the TV series *All Creatures Great and Small*, says, 'When I look in the mirror I see the face of a woman who has been through a lot of pain.'

After a series of inexplicable miscarriages she has finally come to terms with it. 'There doesn't seem to be any gynaecological problem but I have lost several children, usually after about three and a half months of pregnancy,' she says. 'Sometimes it has happened during filming, so it could be to do with lifestyle. When I listen to other actors talking about going home to their kids I find myself thinking – "Oh God, I wish I had children."' However, Carol has now found fulfilment in a new career as a writer.

There is a world of regret in that lament. But childlessness can open up new vistas, new areas for creativity. The energy and time that children take up are all-consuming, so a whole other life can beckon for the older woman without children. Actress Alexandra Bastedo, star of the cult classic *The Champions*, wanted children after marrying her husband at the age of 35. She says, 'You read about women having children in their forties, but it's not that easy. I tried taking drugs. But it was not to be.' Instead she has a sanctuary housing 100 animals, ranging from donkeys, ferrets, koi carp and guinea fowl to geese, hens, ducks, turkeys, chipmunks, Dobermans and cats.

Another actress who rose to fame in a number of television dramas, is case in point. Although the mother of one daughter, she had been trying for another child for many years – and failing, to her great pain. 'I felt a failure,' she says of her inability to conceive a 'later' child. Finally endometriosis, an inflammation of the womb's lining, was diagnosed. 'Knowing I'm less likely to have another child has somehow liberated me to get on with the rest of my life,' she now says.

Many childless older women, however, find that the experience of repeatedly trying and failing becomes in the end, like any bereavement, a lingering sorrow.

Susan Fletcher: Businesswoman

I have one message for your readers: there may not be enough time for you to get pregnant between now and your menopause.

I realise that because of their circumstances, some women only have the opportunity to try for children later on. But you must be aware of the fact that the longer you leave it, the likelihood is that it could be too late and you might not achieve your objective at all.

That's what's happened to me. You do need to be aware. You cannot sit there confidently and say, right, I'm going to wait till I'm 40. If it works that's fantastic. But if you end up having any difficulties, losing babies, taking time afterwards to conceive again, and so on, then you may have got into a situation where is becomes impossible for you.

I think the beginning for me was probably when I was 35. I was married to somebody other than my present husband. I was keen on my career, and was on the Pill. All the press then suggested it was unwise to remain on the Pill beyond the age of 35, which I think is not the case now, as they have a lower dosage one. So, because I was the principal breadwinner in the household, and very focused on my work and also pretty out of touch with my femininity, frankly (as sometimes happens to working women), I thought in terms of getting sterilised.

And in fact I did, encouraged by my husband, who was keen not to have it done himself, as most men are. That caused some problems because I would have preferred that he had. But anyway I went and had it done. I went through all the intellectual side of it and was absolutely convinced it was the right thing to do. What I didn't do, because I was out of touch with myself as a woman, was really try and grasp how I would feel in the aftermath of it.

And I remember so clearly waking up from the anaesthetic and just knowing with every fibre of my being that I had done totally the wrong thing. It completely changed my life. It was when I was coming to, from the anaesthetic, that for once in her life the *woman* within me just came to the surface and said, 'What the hell have you done to me!' It was really like that.

That was the beginning of a very big change. Apart from spending the next six months in all sorts of mental agonies (thinking I should immediately adopt as many children as I could and devote the rest of my life to all that sort of thing), it also gradually, over the course of the next year, allowed the feminine side of my personality to emerge and to assert itself in its proper place in my life.

I think that although I regret in lots and lots of ways having had the operation, I also am so grateful that it did allow that process to begin. Because otherwise I have no idea what I'd be like now. It precipitated a very difficult period between my husband and myself. Subconsciously I blamed him for the predicament I was in. It was very confusing. Then we split up. And then tried to get back together again. And in the meantime I had read a magazine article about fertility. I was told when I was sterilised that was *it*. But I read there were a few possibilities for women in my situation. One was IVF. And the other was to have the operation reversed.

I had gone to the Marie Stopes clinic for contraception before, and I went back and they referred me to the Humana Wellington Private Hospital, where they talked me through all the procedures of both options. And left me thinking I ought to go for IVF. So we tried IVF and it failed. Which it does frequently: I think it's only 1 in 6 that works.

But that in itself was also a very emotional experience and something that I hadn't anticipated. I didn't ever even get to the point where they could implant fertilised eggs. They took my eggs out. But the two they took out didn't get fertilised. I felt gutted.

It is a bereavement. The feeling that you have all this hope. And then it's gone. That was a difficult time. And then I did nothing for a while until I decided that perhaps I ought to have the sterilisation operation reversed. I'd been reluctant, because it's a fairly big operation. In the meantime my husband

and I had decided that we were going to permanently split up. And I had to decide, do I go ahead with this operation? I haven't got a man, etc. And a friend of mine said to me, 'Look, if you do meet somebody, the last thing you want to do at the beginning of a new relationship is go in and have a major operation, particularly of this kind. Just go ahead and do it now.'

I was very, very, lucky that I got referred to Professor Winston at the Hammersmith, who's thought to be one of the best in the country. What they do is they cut across the lower abdomen, right through the abdomen wall and then do microsurgery. The Fallopian tubes are apparently only as thick as cotton thread. They cut out part of the tube that's been clamped through the sterilisation, and then sew back together the edges of this minute tube, leaving the passageway inside clear. You're off work for a month, because it's major stomach surgery.

But I was just so thrilled and so excited, despite all of that. It put me back together again as a woman and I felt very much that I wanted to try to conceive. But of course I was single and 38 by then.

At the Humana Wellington they said that I shouldn't leave it too long. And I kept saying, 'Well, why? People have babies right up until they're 45.' They didn't really elaborate, but I can now see the reason why. If you have difficulties, you can be 40 before you've got anywhere.

It's difficult to break up from a marriage and then just go and drag someone off the street, to mate and marry and spend the rest of your life with. So I decided that I'd try and go ahead and conceive as a single mother. You get so desperate. I had a friend who I wasn't living with, or ever going to live with, who was willing to help me achieve that objective.

We were having an affair. He was married and he knew how desperate I felt. I didn't approach him cold. It was something that we just both knew was there as an issue. And it just sort of happened by time passing, and lots of related and unrelated conversations that led us to that point. He was confident I would be a good mother to any child of his. He was not uninterested. A man can't be. He was happy to be as supportive as he could. He's still with his wife now. At the time that was always likely to be the case. There was no hidden agenda on that.

I did conceive that year, when I was still 38. And I was just so excited. I didn't have an easy pregnancy. But I was so happy, despite all that. I felt elated the whole time. Then I was advised, being 38, that I should have the amnio. And I was told there was a 1 per cent chance of the baby miscarrying. So I had the amnio and two weeks later I went back for my 18-week checkup and the baby was looking healthy and hearty. And then I went back at 22 weeks for another checkup and he'd died some time in between the two. We don't know why. It might have been the amnio, though they say if there is going to be a problem because of the amnio it normally happens within a week.

I fell apart obviously. You have no conception of what you're going to feel like if you lose the baby. I then decided I wasn't strong enough to try again to be a single mother, because if the same thing happened again while I was on my own I didn't think I could cope.

But I had to move forward. And then, miraculously, I met Ian, who is now my husband. He was widowed, with a 13-year-old son. So we got married when I was 40, about two-and-a-half years ago. And the fact that we'd all suffered a bereavement bonded all three of us together. I'd lost a son. James had lost a mother.

We have conceived once, and I lost that baby at seven weeks. I'm not using any contraceptive now but I could have gone in the last year or two to fertility treatments and help on that front. I heard Professor Winston on the radio once say that sometimes he says to couples, 'Give up.' The odds are quite low, and every time you try and you fail it's like a bereavement in some sort of way. It hits you emotionally. And I know exactly what he means. I don't know whether I can cope with any more of that kind of pain.

I just feel desperately lucky that I've got Ian and James. I feel that God's been good to me and why should I ask for more. But whenever people at work are pregnant or their wives are pregnant, or they've just had a baby, I do get terribly emotionally upset. I think intellectually I can rationalise it away. But on the emotional level it's still there. You eventually manage to build a life and move onwards. But you don't ever forget. When I lost Albert [the baby she carried to 22 weeks] I had lots of letters from various people and messages of sympathy. It amazed me how many older women came out with their story.

There was one that stuck in my mind, about an old lady who was in her eighties. She had four children, but there had been a fifth one that had died in the womb. The only one that this woman talked about in her old age was the one that had passed away. And that's not to say that you don't value what you've got, but the one that didn't quite make it is as important to you as a mother in its own way. It has as much impact on you emotionally. The fact that you haven't seen a child through to its potential doesn't stop it from 'staying' with you. It doesn't diminish the impact that child has on your life.

I remember just after it had happened asking a chap who I worked with who had been terribly injured after being in the line of an IRA bomb. I was desperate at the time to find out from people whether I would ever feel better. He said that you get to the point some time after the event where you go through life without any noticeable impact most of the time. But he said he could be in tears in minutes flat if the right buttons get pressed. And I can do that too.

CHAPTER 2

Fit at Fortysomething?

The Medical View

There is no doubt that pregnancy, childbirth and childrearing demand a reasonable level of physical fitness. During gestation and throughout labour, a woman's body undergoes unique changes; she is awash with hormones and subject to extra strain and stress on organs and limbs. There are the hormonal ups and downs, sleeplessness and often frenetic activity of the postnatal period and beyond.

It's not really surprising, then, that some in the medical world are concerned about whether older mothers can cope with the sheer hard graft of the job. There are, too, other issues particularly associated with older mothers: fertility problems, and the well-known risk of bearing a baby with Down's syndrome among other disabilities which are explored in Chapter 7. But in the meantime, is all the caution justified?

In this chapter we will be hearing from four specialists who work in obstetrics, and each gives their answer. But first, we'll look at the history behind today's attitudes, which provides some clues about why motherhood, for older women, is seen by some as an enterprise fraught with danger.

TOO OLD TO ROCK AND ROLL, TOO YOUNG TO DIE

With a real show of spirit Nancy, Lady Astor, once said, 'I refuse to admit I'm more than 52, even if that does make my sons illegitimate.' And in fact the middle years of life, when one is past the full bloom of youth but nowhere near dotage, are a long stretch that can be among the most contented and fruitful of our lives. Gone are the insecurities and growing pains of the semi-adult; yet to come are the physical and economic uncertainties of old age.

Our attitudes to ageing are complex. At the very root of the issue is a primitive fear of death. Nearly as potent is the fear of decrepitude, which brings with it a creeping sense of uselessness. We in the West have a less than generous attitude to the elderly: the old among us seem to be discarded so easily. Yet the process of ageing is one that comes to most of us. Each bag, each sag, each wrinkle moves us inexorably closer to that moment in time when death will claim us.

The thought of death may not be at the very top of our minds when waking in the morning and groaning at the sight in the bathroom mirror. Ordinary life can't be sustained if one is indulging in a constant internal monologue of such philosophic magnitude. However, from that basic, if submerged, knowledge, all else follows.

It explains the billions of pounds spent by women in the West on cosmetics. These are not just to improve; they are to disguise. And what they disguise is, as Milton put it, 'the silent touches' of Father Time. It is true that some women are luckier than others in the genetic stakes. Gloria Steinem was once complimented by a rather effusive reporter who remarked on how good she looked at (God forbid) 50. 'But,' she said, 'this *is* 50. This is what 50 looks like. We just wouldn't recognize it.'

For the most part, we live in a youth-oriented culture. It's advisable to look as youthful as you can because it is the young who inherit the earth – or at least, if not the earth, then the jobs, the opportunities, the future. In the coming years this is gradually going to change, as the make-up of our population shifts. Soon there will be more people aged over 60 than under, and the boot will be on the other foot (or if not the boot, then certainly the vote).

For now, however, the cult of youth is supreme, and until very recently the older mother was considered at enormous risk and a very real medical aberration. But here again the sheer volume of numbers has confounded the medics, simply because more and more women are doing it – and not just that, but doing it successfully.

Attitudes to the older mother have softened; but residual reservations remain. There is still a prejudice against the older mother that goes over and above immediate worries about potential physical and mental disabilities in the foetus. It is usually unspoken, but it lies silently at the heart of the matter. It is simply that this 'vessel', seen as an aged and shrivelling body, cannot be the right place to plant and nurture something as vulnerable as a tiny seed. Old crumbling womb. New, tiny, fragile life. The two cannot be combined. They are antithetical.

The medical term used to describe the older woman having her first child – elderly primigravida – itself carries a slight chill. 'Primigravida' is a combination of the Latin for 'first' and 'heavy' (or 'pregnant'); and, aside from the depressing use of the word 'elderly' in the term, 'gravida' resonates unnervingly with 'gravity' and 'grave'. It's enough to make you cross your legs.

For this elderly primigravida, then, pregnancy is a voyage into the unknown hedged about with question marks and qualifications. Not for her the comforting, though superficial, props of make-up and role-enhancing fashion. Though these may clothe the person they do not hide the facts. There, clearly written on her medical record is her birthdate. There she is, situated fairly and squarely in the group with the flashing red light above them. With the passage of time, she has been rendered less and less able than her younger sisters to bear children successfully. Or at least that is what 'informed opinion' would have us believe.

More and more women are proving that opinion wrong. One can understand the concerns of the medics. The fitness and general good health of a mother is of paramount importance, and it's their job to look after her during childbirth. Many of them are doubtless influenced by powerful images from the past, when serious concern about the older mother were justified. But it's dangerous to allow past performance to determine current thinking. It becomes increasingly meaningless to compare the physiology of women now with the physiology of women then, when we know how radically altered are women's lives.

ONE BORN EVERY YEAR

How many women do you know who have given birth 15 times?

That's what many women did as a matter of course, as recently as the 1920s. No wonder that by the time they were in their later childbearing years, their twentieth confinement killed them. It *was* dangerous, then, to give birth in your middle years, but that's undoubtedly because a woman's obstetric profile could well have been drastically compromised by her long list of past pregnancies.

Knowing that, the following extract from Samuel Pepys' Diary, from 1662, makes some sense.

25 May. Lords day... To church and heard a good sermon of Mr Woodcockes at our church. Only, in his later prayer for a woman in childbed, he prayed that God would deliver her from the hereditary curse of childebearing, which seemed a pretty strange expression.

It may have seemed strange to Pepys, but perhaps not to the woman.

Women these days lead different lives. A fit, well-nourished 40-year-old is an altogether different medical proposition from the wasted and worn women who have preceded us. Health care, too, now is improved beyond recognition. Advances in medical technology save lives daily that would have had no chance in even the recent past. In the West, women generally have more food, more money and a better knowledge of sanitation.

In years gone by, mothers were more susceptible to all forms of illness and disease. Weakened by years of constant childbearing, childrearing, poor nutrition and hygiene, they were prey to the slightest germ or virus, and at the mercy of any constitutional weaknesses. No wonder they died in droves, and their children were sickly.

We've had a hint of how awful conditions were in Pepys' day. Things had not improved dramatically, for many, by the Victorian era, when people still paid for their health care. Levels of well-being were well below the standards of today. With many mouths to feed, families either couldn't pay for doctors, and suffered, or waited till the eleventh, and by then often fatal, hour, before calling someone in. The longer the wait, the more complicated the return to health. The older the woman, the less her chance of surviving. Such must have been their desperation, that the following superstition unearthed by Iona and Peter Opie for their book, *Babies: An Unsentimental Anthology*, is hardly surprising:

> If you rock an empty cradle, you will rock a new baby into it. This is a superstition *in viridi observantia*, and it is quite curious to see the face of alarm with which a poor woman, with her tenth baby in her arms, will dash across a room to prevent the 'baby-but-one' from engaging in such a dangerous amusement as rocking the empty cradle.
>
> *The Book of Days* by Robert Chambers (1864)

Although there were antenatal clinics in some areas by that time, many women did not attend, and few contacted a doctor or midwife until well into the pregnancy. If there were complications – and the greater the number of pregnancies any woman has, the greater the complications – they wouldn't be picked up soon enough.

In the 19th century, many women also continued working long hours in factories and mills while pregnant. While doing some research into breastfeeding, I came across the fact that once women who worked in factories had given birth, their babyminder, probably an elderly neighbour or even one of their older children, would bring the baby into the factory for a feed which the woman would do while still standing at, and probably working, her machine. When breastfeeding, many women literally feel the energy draining out of their body. To breastfeed while working a machine during a factory shift is almost beyond belief.

Work of a different kind waited for them, of course, when they got back and took on the enormous responsibility of hearth, home, and other children. Life was hard, diet poor, and rest, sleep and comfort for the pregnant woman rare. Infant and maternal mortality were both high.

In certain areas, real poverty, and the awful conditions for women that go with it, persisted well into the 20th century. My aunt was a midwife in the northeast of England, one of the poorest areas in Britain. She talked of being called out to homes when a woman was in labour. Always she would ask for boiling water. With great solemnity, the chip pan would be scraped out of its fat and water would be boiled and ceremoniously 'sterilised' in it. She spoke, too, of babies born so poorly that it was the midwife's job to go quietly into a corner with the ailing infant, where she would place a hand over both its nose and its mouth until it was dead.

We can only assume that many women did not want a life wracked by multiple births and high rates of infant death, because many without access to contraceptive advice were driven to seek refuge in pills and potions to 'solve' their problems. Back-street abortions also created havoc with women's bodies. Where knitting needles weren't used, slivers of slippery elm twig were often employed, pushed up into the vagina to induce miscarriage.

Living conditions were appalling. A survey of York in 1935 found that 31 per cent of the population lived below the poverty line, 14 per cent of those in 'abject' poverty. Many millions of families lived in slum dwellings. In Leeds there were 75,000 back-to-back dwellings, 33,000 of which were unfit for human habitation. We may hear now about the great community spirit and the sharing and caring that went on in close neighbourhoods in 'the good old days'. This communal spirit was just as well, because whole families lived together in one or two rooms, in decaying houses sharing one lavatory and one water tap among 40 or 50 people. Nutrition was so poor that the underprivileged were prone to rickets, dental caries, anaemia and infectious diseases such as tuberculosis.

Haven't we all seen the television reports of women in famine-hit 'developing' countries, nourishing her child from a pathetically wizened breast, or dealing out desperately small portions of food for the family? And we know they will take even less for themselves. It can't have been any different (and probably still isn't) in this country. After a couple of decades of such belt-tightening, imagine the health of the older mother.

With such a backdrop to older motherhood, it isn't surprising that prejudices linger. But aside from doubts cast on women's physical capacity to bear a child, there are others which, though unspoken, are nonetheless apparent. One of the most pernicious is the idea that the older mother is less capable, psychologically, to nurture and parent. (Less capable than what, one muses as we catch sight of this or that vile abuse perpetrated on innocent children of all ages, by parents of all ages?) But nevertheless, there is the view that older parents some-how, just by the very fact of being older, shortchange their offspring in a way that younger parents do not.

Do older parents lack that vital spark? Are their children neglected as they grow elderly and seem to lose their appetite for life? Are those parents so out of huff and puff that their children are confined to a life of torpor and inactivity? Or are these children treated like hothouse flowers, overprotected and overindulged, turned into precious treasures by doting, ageing parents? Are these children embarrassed beyond endurance when picked up at the school gates by a greyhaired mum most people mistake for their granny?

In fact, parents who are older could be more, rather than less fit to parent, because of the very fact of their advanced years. Researcher Rachel Cook of City University in London told the latest annual meeting of the British Psychological Society that parents of children conceived by IVF or donor insemination make more loving, caring couples with a greater emotional involvement in their families.

Some of these people will be older by the time they become parents, simply because of the years it can take to first recognise fertility problems, and then surmount the various bureaucratic and medical hurdles that are all part of IVF and donor insemination. Many older parents who conceive have had to wait for a long time to have their children too, and naturally in a sense that is like working harder. Their children have not come easy. It would seem from the research that it is those who have not found it easy who relish and sustain their children most lovingly.

MEDICALLY SPEAKING ...

Again and again I have heard doctors say that if an older woman is physically fit, with good stamina and a healthy diet, her pregnancy is more likely to be trouble-free than that of a younger woman who does not look after herself. But the physical risks remain and it is the job of the obstetric specialists to guide us as safely as they can through the dangers that can lie in wait.

Four people who deliver help to the pregnant woman,

and in particular the older one, speak in the following pages. The first two are fertility specialists, the last two, a midwife and a yoga instructor. Each has a very individual view of the older mother.

Dr Gill Lockwood: Clinical Research Fellow in Infertility, John Radcliffe Hospital, Oxford

I think the gut reaction to this age issue is almost an aesthetic one. It is this notion of the smooth-skinned Madonna with the baby at the breast bit. As someone recently said, the idea of wrinklies with babies at their breasts is somehow tacky and unpleasant. This seems to me to be desperately unfair.

The older mother issue does turn upside down quite a lot of other notions that society has got about what it is appropriate for women to be doing at various stages of their lives. For instance, society has had great difficulty coming to terms with working women. It had great difficulty coming to terms with daughters no longer being the property of their fathers to be disposed of as they saw fit, and the idea I suppose of fertility and fecundity has always been perceived by a male-dominated society as sort of woman's secret weapon.

I am going to overstate the point, but men have always rather resented the fact that at the end of the day, their way of perpetuating their genes for their dynastic or family interests, depended upon a woman. And this gave women the ultimate influence over things that maybe men, because they like to control everything, thought they should be able to control as well.

This ties in with why men resisted contraception to

such an extent: because it gave women a power they didn't like them having. If women's fertility and fecundity become to be seen as a choice and an option that they can control, and in the case of the older mother, prolong, this is again expanding their power in an area where men already feel quite uncomfortable.

Although it is rare for women in their forties to conceive naturally, it's not unknown. And you could possibly argue that if society hadn't for so long placed such a premium on *young* motherhood, there might perhaps be a different climate now for older mothers.

The woman trying for a baby in her late thirties, who finds she's having difficulty conceiving, can be doubly disadvantaged. First, nature has ordained that we should have babies when we are doing GCSEs because that's when fertility peaks. But this woman also comes up against the almost sociological brick wall that says that society's vision of motherhood is a teenaged Madonna.

If you were to look at this from a feminist angle, you couldn't help noticing, for instance, that nobody thinks it's awful when a Hollywood film star fathers his nineteenth child at the age of sixtysomething. There's much backslapping. That's the Jack Nicholson/Warren Beatty brigade. And of course Charlie Chaplin's last baby was conceived in his eightieth year.

If you are trying to make sociological sense of this phenomenon, with women's life expectancy being what it is, and the fact that women enjoy good health and don't look old at the point that they once did, you have to realise that something fundamental has shifted. You've only got to go to a Third World country and see women who are actually in their thirties and forties but look much older. And still look presumably as we would have done if we had the poor diet and healthcare they have.

The medical situation is that the older woman can cope with pregnancy just as well as a younger woman. The fundamental point is that the biological activity of pregnancy is so overwhelming, physiologically, that the relatively minor differences in physiology between a 25-year-old and a 40-year-old are nothing compared to the enormous differences in physiology that are actually imposed by the pregnant state itself.

So the extra weight, the extra strain that's put on the circulation and heart, lungs and kidneys that comes from being 45 years old as opposed to 25 years old is trivial compared to, for instance, the increase in the volume of blood circulation, which goes up 50 per cent as a result of being pregnant. Or the doubling of the work that the kidneys have to do to deal with, effectively, two bodies' worth of waste products, rather than just one.

That is one reason why people have blown up out of all proportion the risks that the older woman runs in pregnancy. If she embarks on pregnancy in a healthy state, her pregnancy should not be hazardous. The view I take with my patients, who for whatever reason are older, is that nature operates its own selection process.

Oxford is the classic place where everybody plans to become chairman of the board and then decides to have their first baby at 37. That's part of their career plan. What I've said to them is that nature is acting as an almost natural screen. The people who *do* conceive

readily, later than average, are likely to have as easy
and as successful a pregnancy as younger women. It
is almost nature's test of biological fitness, if you like,
how easily a body can succeed in conceiving. If you
conceive and get through those first early months
without miscarriage, and don't lose your baby your
body has decided you can carry to term, your
pregnancy should be straightforward.

We know the conditions that are associated with
difficulty in conceiving, like diabetes, and high blood
pressure and fibroids. Indeed, all the rest of those
conditions that are held out as warnings to the older
mother. But the function of those conditions is that
they are automatically screening out women who
would have difficulty carrying a pregnancy to term
anyway. This is classic Darwinian evolutionary
theory. It is true that as you get older the proportion
of women with fibroids will increase. But if the
fibroids aren't causing enough trouble to interfere
with successful implantation in the first place, the
chance that they're going to so prejudice your
pregnancy is tiny.

High blood pressure, pre-eclampsia, is a problem,
but in fact as a condition, it is also increased in very
young women and in women who are overweight.
And very often the sort of successful professional
women who are embarking very sensibly on a first
pregnancy in their late thirties or early forties will
have had their pre-conceptual counselling, will have
had their folic acid, will have got their weight into the
perfect range. They will probably be fit and much
suppler than in fact they would be otherwise.

This is a minor point, but it's my very young
women who get terrible stretch marks and varicose

veins and bad backs, all the things that older mothers are supposed to suffer from. Their young skin in fact doesn't stretch as readily as old skin. And the posture of a woman who's exercised regularly, and has spent 20 years holding herself up straight (so that she can impress the interview committee), is much better, and less likely to lead to aches and pains during pregnancy. It's my poor little teenage mums who live entirely on crisps and cigarettes that I have to worry about, rather than the lawyers and university lecturers who come for early pregnancy monitoring.

I work in the area of fertility, where the issue of the appropriate age for women to stop bearing children is a much debated one. At its most extreme, you may remember the furore about the 59-year-old British businesswoman who went to Italy and became one of the first postmenopausal mothers in this country. She went to a doctor called Professor Antinori in Rome who has some very interesting findings on the health of postmenopausal women during their pregnancies.

He found out that when he looked at the health outcomes for the women he treated, if he screened out those who were unfit at the start, then the egg donation IVF women, the postmenopausal mothers, did just as well in terms of pregnancy complications and childbirth complications as a matched group of younger women. The screening-out criteria he used when selecting which older mothers should undergo egg donor IVF was exactly the same as that used to screen out younger women attempting a pregnancy.

A lot of the arguments that were presented at the time against this much older mother and her test tube twins, particularly in the tabloids, was about who was going to look after her children. In fact her then partner, now husband of many years, is 20 years younger than she is. So there was no question at all of the children being left entirely without a natural parent. Also, this woman was a self-made millionaire. There are all the resources necessary to care for these children.

She had spent some time pursuing the possibility of egg donation IVF in this country and had been turned down, so took herself off to Rome. As it happens, the tide has turned against Professor Antinori in Italy, where his work with post-menopausal women has just been made illegal. Quite unfairly, because the idea that every postmenopausal woman is going to be clamouring to have a baby when she should be dandling grandchildren on her knee is ludicrous.

There are a very small minority of women who want postmenopausal fertility treatment. For those few who do, it can be for a number of reasons. They may want a baby perhaps because they've been unable to reconcile themselves to the loss of another child, or they've been ill and they have missed the boat biologically. They may have been infertile for years due to illness, but when cured can turn from being a chronic invalid into a perfectly healthy normal woman, who now wants to do what the vast majority of perfectly normal healthy women want to do, and that's have a baby.

The whole rapid development of IVF technology has put a lot of people into the situation of just missing a chance to have a child. If a woman is now in her forties, that sense of anguish and loss can be enormous. Some breakthroughs have come just too late for her and they are in the position of knowing that if only these developments had happened even two years ago their lives would have been different. It seems to me to be completely unacceptable to take what it says on somebody's birth certificate as a way of making what is essentially a very significant personal decision. If it says that you're 45 then in quite a lot of clinics you can be offered egg donation IVF. But if you're 46 you can't. I am very concerned about the disadvantage suffered by one-sixth of the population that can't, because of fertility problems, become parents when they want, where they want and with whoever they want.

Lastly, the whole question of having to justify why we want children is an enormous one. The way that I've always explained people's need for children and how it isn't always the same for everyone, is that the clock that runs in a woman's head doesn't follow Greenwich Mean Time. Some little girls go straight from wanting to play with dolls, to playing with babies and it's entirely appropriate for them to start thinking of having babies in their teens. But the older woman is often expected to justify her desire for a child. I don't think that it is appropriate for anyone to make judgements about why a person wants a child. To say to a woman, 'Oh, you've got a successful career . . . ' or, 'Your new husband's got children by his ex-wife', or even 'At least you've got *one*'. I think that is something where you do almost need to have a second X chromosome (i.e. be a woman) to understand. I have encountered a lot of difficulty explaining much of this to my predominantly male colleagues. So, if you want to take a fanciful model, you could say that desiring a child starts a particular clock in a woman's brain, and that clock's time runs quite independently of any other timescale that may be going on.

It's a completely inappropriate area for moral judgements to come into play. Moral judgements should operate in the area of how people look after their babies when they've got them. Society is so reluctant to step in and take a baby or child into care, even if the most outrageous parenting is going on, *if* the baby is conceived 'naturally'. And yet perfectly reasonable, sensible, calm, kindly, well-intentioned couples feel they have to justify to me that they'll be better than average parents before they can even go on the waiting list for treatment that typically has only a 1 in 4 chance of working on each given cycle.

It's not surprising that people with an intractable fertility problem seem to be a little bit crazy. They're facing odds that would be completely unacceptable in any other walk of life. If every time I took out an appendix, I only got it right 25 per cent of the time, I would be struck off the medical register. And yet when I do IVF and I get a baby in one out of four cycles, that's the best success rate in the world.

The grief of the woman who doesn't have a child is immense. Society is getting a bit better at acknowledging it. But for most people who have a long-standing fertility problem, it remains hidden. Often to the extent that they try and justify not being parents, by not wanting to be parents, because it is a source of such pain.

When Virginia Bottomley, as Health Minister, said, 'Nobody ever dies of being infertile, therefore we don't need to fund fertility treatments,' what she's not allowing for is the number of lives that are so damaged, that a physical illness would be much easier to cope with. I sometimes think with some of my patients that if I said, 'Well, if I chop off your right hand, then I can almost guarantee you'll have a baby,' they would hold it out for me and say, 'Do it.'

Richard Howell: Consultant Gynaecologist, Homerton Hospital, Hackney and the Portland Hospital, London

I'm changing my attitudes as I get older, and also as I'm seeing more women asking for children in older age. I started off in the field of fertility treatment, about eight years ago, and my attitude then was that there should be a cut-off limit when a woman got to 40. I was worried about older women bringing up teenagers, and also about the children having very old parents.

On top of that, I was worried about the obstetric complications in the over-forties. That's not only the chromosomal defects, but the high rates of miscarriage, diabetes and increased incidence of complications such as pre-eclampsia. Also it's just much more knackering going through pregnancy in your forties than in your thirties.

The first trimester, the first 12 weeks, there is likely to be a higher rate of miscarriage. This is probably due to chromosomal abnormalities which result in spontaneous loss of the baby. Then, of course, the woman is subject to all the rigours of antenatal screening.

An older woman is likely to have higher blood pressure at the start of her pregnancy. And as blood pressure goes up anyway in pregnancy, there's a risk that it'll go higher still.

The placenta doesn't work as well in older women, so the pre-eclampsia I've mentioned becomes a combination of high blood pressure, protein in the urine and swelling. Because older women tend to produce these poorer placentas, as their uterus is not as young as it was, the afterbirth doesn't work so well. They're more prone to interuterine growth retardation – the small baby syndrome.

Diabetes is a condition of older age. And older mothers can develop that too. Diabetes in pregnancy can lead to problems of large babies, small babies or stillbirth.

Then there's the labour itself. Labour can be more difficult. The uterus may not contract as well. The labour is more likely to be incoordinate. Therefore the chances of induction and/or Caesarean section is higher.

The older woman is more likely to have fibroids. Endometriosis is also a problem for the older mother. That's where the lining of the womb, instead of coming out of the vagina at the time of period, travels along the Fallopian tubes and implants in the pelvic cavity. It leads to painful periods, painful intercourse and irregular bleeding. If these conditions exist in the older woman to begin with, they will have had more time to develop and get worse. In fact, any chronic, debilitating disease is more likely to worsen by the time a woman approaches her middle years.

Breastfeeding I don't think is a problem, though again the exhaustion factor comes in there.

This is where the older woman can do so much to help herself. If she's fit she can cope much better. But I don't think you can *get* pregnant as easily. However much exercise you take, your eggs are still going to age.

We don't know exactly what it is about an aged egg that is different from a younger one. All we do know is that they don't fertilise so well. The sperm will go up to them and try and penetrate them and they can't get through. Or they may fertilise but they just don't develop properly. The same is not true of sperm, that can go on for years. It has to be said, though, that there is now evidence that men over the age of 45, fathering children, run a high risk of having babies with problems.

There's quite a useful concept that a friend of mine is using. At his hospital, instead of taking into account the absolute age of the woman, they're taking into account the mean age of the couple. So if you had a 44-year-old woman and she has a 55-year-old husband, then they would almost certainly exclude her from any treatment. But if that woman had got a 30-year-old partner, then their mean age is 37, and they'd help treat them. That begins to exclude my worries of older parents bringing up teenagers. As long as one parent is there it helps.

For all those reasons I have concerns for the older mother in general, but also in particular, concerns about offering fertility treatment to the over-forties. IVF treatment *per se* is not very effective over the age of 40. Beyond then there's only about a 10 per cent pregnancy success rate. And in fact, if you're normally fertile, if you have a normal partner's sperm, you have open tubes and you're ovulating and you have a healthy venue where eggs and sperm can meet, you are much more likely to get pregnant by natural conception over 40 than you are by IVF treatment.

IVF does not turn back the clock. Do not look to it

as a treatment for old age. Women who come to see me for fertility treatment have a fertility problem. If they've got blocked tubes, their only alternative is for IVF. But if a woman just comes at the age of 44 say, and would like to conceive and is having problems, there is little that IVF can offer to hasten that.

Egg donation is a separate issue. The reason that women over 40 are not getting pregnant is because their eggs are of poorer quality. If we can get egg donation going, then success rates are reasonable. We're talking about a 20 to 25 per cent pregnancy rate. But that is not the child of the woman. That is an egg, or more likely eggs, from someone else, who is young, under the age of 36, so there is less risk of Down's. She would be of proven fertility preferably, but not necessarily, and can be a friend, or relative, or unknown.

You get her eggs and fertilise them with the sperm of the older woman's husband or partner, and then you have to freeze the embryos. It's not legally binding that they be frozen. But if you're talking about embryos from an unrelated, unknown donor, then you've got to think in terms of HIV incubation. There is a potential risk of transmission of HIV. What you do then is HIV test the donor, keep the embryos on ice and retest the donor six months later; then you know you've got HIV negative embryos.

In general, most of the women I deal with are successful professional women who've always had a career. Who often denied ever wanting children, or at least put it on the back burner. They get to the age of 39 or 40 and think, 'Oh shit! Time's run out. If I'm going to have a baby I've got to have one *now*.' And then they get very businesslike. They get all the investigations done, and treatment as soon as possible. They can't waste a month and they go hell for leather.

It's a very demanding group of patients. They're usually very well versed in the topic. Done a lot of reading round it and feel that they can't miss a single day. Then you get to the 'mid-cycle syndrome'. That's when their partners are fully aware of their cycle. They know that when they get home from work on this or that particular night, they've got to perform because it's day 13, or 14, of the cycle. This leads to relationship and sexual problems. The men start to feel like machines, sperm banks. They start to dread the middle of the month, because they *have* to perform. And if a man *has* to perform, sometimes, it doesn't work. There's pressurisation from the woman. The man resents being an object rather than a person. Sex happens mid-cycle only. And often the men are not as motivated as the women to have a child in the first place.

Postmenopausal mothers are another issue. I will see anybody for consultation currently who is still menstruating, to discuss the issue and talk about success rates. I have problems with the postmenopausal woman: pregnant in her fifties and bringing a teenager up in her seventies. Teenagers are demanding. She may well be able to go through pregnancy with obstetric complications which are not horrendous. Though she'll probably be exhausted. You've got to think why does that woman want to have a child. It's a very selfish thing in a way.

Perhaps all couples *wanting* children are selfish. But is the postmenopausal woman really thinking of the child? Or herself? Is she looking for comfort, postmenopausally? Is she trying to bring back her youth? Or have some form of security for her old age?

But for the woman in her forties, I have seen some whose lives have been transformed by having a child. Professional women, whose lives were urban, workaholic, sophisticated, working all hours, out to dinner every night, socialising, having too much to drink at weekends and enjoying life to the full. But something deep inside them was lacking. They were unhappy. When they get pregnant and have a baby then their whole life transforms. They give up work. They become a mum, and radiant. I've seen it.

I think an older mother can be a better mother than she might have been when she was younger. Many of the older women who are having children now, would have made bloody awful mothers in their twenties. Most of us in our forties were just getting going with our lives in the late 1960s and 1970s. We were rebellious in those days. We were all doing all sorts of stupid things. I think they would have made bad mothers then. Perhaps they've grown up.

Ina May Gaskin, whose thoughts follow, works as a renowned midwife in Tennessee. She has written a well-received book called *Spiritual Midwifery*. Here she puts down her thoughts on 'late bloomers', as she calls them – the women who give birth after the age of 35.

Ina May Gaskin: Midwife

We are living in times in which increasing numbers of women are waiting until relatively late in their reproductive lives to give birth for the first time. Most midwifery and obstetrical services have seen a significant rise in the number of first-time mothers over the age of 35.

Orthodox medical education has traditionally treated the mother over 35 as inherently high risk, particularly if the mother is giving birth to her first child. Medical students are warned that these women are more likely to be obese, hypertensive, to have fibromas or to have cardiovascular disease. Future obstetricians may easily get the idea just from the terminology that is customarily used in their education that any mother over 35 may not be able to give birth unaided by technology.

While I do recognise that many women are not in good physical shape by their thirty-fifth birthdays, and may need certain kinds of interventions in order to give birth safely, it is also true that just as many women are in very good condition in their late thirties and into their forties, especially nowadays, when exercise and good self-care have become fashionable.

To consider an entire age category of women high risk, regardless of whether the individual women do indeed suffer from the various problems that have been associated with older women who are pregnant, is to be practising a very crude and unscientific brand of obstetrics. Any midwife or physician who is attentive and well trained ought to be able to detect the woman who is hypertensive or suffers from cardiovascular problems. I can think of no good reason why all women in this age category should be given the idea that pregnancy and birth for them should be fraught with danger.

The trouble with this concept is that it makes no allowance for the maturity of attitude that older women frequently have, which can be a great help to a woman in labour. I have found that certain women over 35 are less apt than younger women sometimes are to waste time and precious energy during labour by feeling sorry for themselves or by fighting labour. A woman with a mature attitude is usually able to use the energy of labour efficiently, and to rest effectively while dilating, or in between pushes.

I would also mention the woman who takes better care of herself at the age of 40 plus than she did as a younger woman. I recently attended the birthing of a woman who became pregnant for the first time at the age of 42. Around the age of 40, she had begun to be very conscientious about eating a good diet – plenty of protein, fresh fruits and vegetables and grains. Not many months after she began eating well, she had become pregnant.

She went into labour at 39 weeks. After about five hours of active labour, her cervix was fully dilated. At first, she was unable to push effectively, partly because she didn't know that it would ease the pain if she pushed when it was the most intense, and also because she was tired and hadn't thought that we midwives would allow her to eat while in labour.

When she mentioned that she thought she would be stronger if she got something to eat, we got her what she wanted. She drank nearly three-quarters of a quart of herbal tea, and remarkably, ate four or five tablespoonsful of peanut butter in between pushes. Once she had eaten her fill, she was able to push in a very co-ordinated fashion, and her baby was soon born with no damage to her perineum. I believe that this woman's smooth labour and delivery – and I'm comparing her with all first-time mothers, not just those over the age of 35 – is attributable to her good *nutrition* and to her excellent attitude about pregnancy and giving birth. The mature woman who has really given up on the idea of becoming pregnant, who is then blessed with a pregnancy, has a high threshold of pain and a giving attitude, which combine to enable her to give birth with maximum efficiency.

A different mother had her first child at the age of 38 after a couple of years of fertility workups. Her pregnancy was very normal, and although this woman was somewhat overweight, she was physically active, and her muscle tone was good. She had no problems with hypertension, so we judged that she would be a safe candidate for home birth.

This woman's labour was in no way distinguished by her age. Because she had for years lived among other women who had given birth without anaesthesia, her expectation was that she could too, so we didn't go through a period of her doubting that she could endure the process of birth. Her entire labour took about 10 hours, and her baby was born over an intact perineum.

In conclusion, I would say that first-time mothers over 35 deserve to be treated as individuals. It seems to me that protocols which state that age alone is a complicating factor in childbirth are too simplistic to fit the reality of childbearing women.

Lolly Stirk: Yoga Teacher and Childbirth Educator

What comes to my mind when I think of the women I have worked with who are older than the average is the word 'precious'. All babies are precious. But the pregnancies and babies for these women are absolutely precious. They were definitely glowing during their pregnancies. They looked wonderful.

Two of them who I knew as older mothers hadn't met the right guys before and they had fallen madly in love at around 40 and had both fallen pregnant. One thing I realised was, as these women were well into their forties, if they had gone along the NHS route, they would have been treated as a problem. And they could have had difficulty. Because as soon as you're seen as a problem you usually start to act like one. Or things do start happening that are difficult.

And luckily these women had the money to go to à private hospital that did not view them as problems. It was a place that was very openminded. They were prepared to let the pregnancies unfold, to see what happens. But interestingly, these two ladies had led lives where they took great care of themselves generally and in my yoga classes they were the fittest. Their bodies were in even better shape than some of the 20-year-olds.

They had the most incredibly ordinary births. They delivered in water to help with the pain and got through the labour and birth very well. And afterwards they were wonderful mothers.

Towards the end of the pregnancies, with the women I'm thinking of, there was a slight problem of blood pressure. When it started to show all of them took it really easy, and looked after themselves in a way that younger mothers sometimes don't. They weren't surprised by it. And they set up therapies like acupuncture, and all the things that can be used to naturally help blood pressure remain stable. They all managed to get to the labour without being induced, and it was exceptional because the last couple of weeks were a real strain. But there was a kind of calmness they had.

But it can be difficult for older women. One older mother I can think of had an awful time with her first birth many years before. She'd been in a very 'high-tech' hospital and was very, very afraid of being drawn into that again. So she asked me to be her birth partner to kind of protect her.

I went round to her home when the labour started, at about 2.00am. We were just getting ready to go to the hospital. And what happened wasn't anything that I would ever choose or advise. But it was such a satisfying experience for her the second time round. It was so fast! I asked her what she wanted to do. 'Well, maybe I'll just hang around for a little while,' she said. She was so *compos mentis*. She was not like many women are when they are coming to giving birth, which is off in another world really. I lay down on the couch and said 'I'll see you soon.'

So she went to the bedroom and apparently lay down and within about 10 minutes she was having these incredibly strong contractions. She went to the bathroom because she felt enormous pressure and I went through and saw she was doing so well breathing through the contractions and relaxing between. I said to her husband, 'Go and get the car.' But while he was gone I saw there was no holding this baby back.

As soon as he walked back into the bathroom she turned her back to him and he held her under her armpits, so her body was upright, sort of standing with her knees bent and her legs curling onto the floor. I knelt down on the floor. And just *caught* this baby. It flew out at me. It was lovely. You know when you see them catching rugby balls! It was like, whooooooomph! It landed right in my chest. Then she stepped over into the bath, which was empty. And I sat on the edge of the bath and held the baby over my legs, leaning forwards to let all the mucus and amniotic fluid drain.

But I knew the baby hadn't started breathing, and I started to stroke it and blow on it. Which I did instinctively. It suddenly juddered, gasping inwards and it began breathing. It felt a bit like lighting a fire. When you blow on the flames to get them going.

Her placenta came tumbling out about five minutes later. That was after I had told her husband to suck her nipples. The poor guy. He said, 'Whaaat!' I said, 'Just suck her nipples because you know sucking nipples helps the womb to contract.' It stimulates the release of oxytocin which will help stop the bleeding so there's less likelihood of haemorrhaging.

Afterwards, she went to the hospital to be checked out, but all was fine. And she has since had another baby. The first was when she was 43, and this last one was at 46. This time round she did exceptionally well as well. It went swiftly and was fine.

She'd been told by her GP the first time that she probably would have a Caesarean. So she went and told him after that it had gone all right. And he just said, 'That was a very dangerous thing to do. Not to make sure you were in the hospital in time.' They won't let you win . . .

There can be such a prejudice about older mothers. The ones I have worked with have, without exception, been very fit. But it could be that a woman who does not look after herself and gets pregnant at

40 and beyond *does* have a more difficult time. But that's the problem with the big NHS machine. They have great difficulty in seeing people as individuals. So all they see on a form is 40, and you are immediately cited as a problem.

For the older mother, it's so precious, as I've said. And you've probably thought it's not going to happen, and then when it *does* happen, it's just like Christmas and Easter and your birthday all rolled into one. Everything. It's a new life.

CHAPTER 3

Older Mother, New Society

We've seen a little of how older motherhood looks from the inside, and have heard the medics' view. But what of the older mother as she is seen by society?

It's perhaps a truism that the nuclear family is in a state of flux. Many couples choose never to marry. Others opt for the child-free life. The ranks of single parents are swelling. And as we know, growing numbers of older women are having babies. So, having 'arrived' as a phenomenon, older mothers now appear, like the other societal mavericks, neatly categorised in statistical tables.

We've heard that many older women are delaying having children to consolidate their careers, or to cement a second relationship. But what is it that is happening to help shape these decisions?

This chapter looks at social trends which begin to fill in the background of our image of today's older mother.

NUCLEAR MELTDOWN?

In the introduction to this book we saw that the average age for mothers has now risen to 28.1. According to the latest report in *Population Trends*, published by the Office of Population Censuses and Surveys, births to women over 40 have risen by half again in the last 10 years. The birth rate among those in their twenties is declining.

Many of the older women having babies are doing so outside the traditional context of Mum-Dad-and-2.5 children – the nuclear family. Among the fortysomething mothers, the highest rise in births has been in those to unmarried women – up nearly three times between 1983 and 1993. The over-forties is the only age group of women in which the unmarried are more likely to have babies than the married.

Dr Kathleen Kiernan, a specialist in family issues at the London School of Economics, has said, 'These women are highly educated professionals who remain childless well into their thirties, building up their careers. What we don't know is whether they are delaying so long by choice. After the age of 35 it takes longer to conceive and the risk of miscarriage is greater. It could be that having decided to delay and then taking longer to conceive they are being shunted past 40.'

Dr Jennifer Kidd, a psychologist specialising in occupational issues at London University's Birkbeck College, believes these women leave less to chance, speculating that 'better qualified women know that if they want to get back to work after having their families they need to consolidate their skills first. They want to be in a better position in an increasingly competitive labour market.'

In years gone by, the births that did occur to women in the older age range were in general to those women still building their families. What is emerging from the OPCS figures is that a larger proportion in the last decade have been to older women starting their families.

It seems as if women are hedging their bets more than they used to. They may be in long relationships and even marriages in their twenties and early thirties, but more and more of them are holding off having children till later. And more than 1 in 4 births inside marriage to the over-forties in 1992 were to remarried women, up 5 per cent on a decade earlier. Also in that year, first and second babies accounted for more than 40 per cent of births to remarried women, compared with 29 per cent in 1983. Greater numbers of these women are starting their childbearing in a second or later marriage.

Jo Hodder, whose story follows, has two sons from an early marriage; but her remarriage to a man some 15 years her junior, and the birth of their child when she was 42, have given her a brand-new lease of life.

Jo Hodder: Housewife, Mother

I had my first son when I was 20. He's now 25. And my second son when I was 23. He's 22 now. My husband is 30. He was nearly 23 when we started going out together. I was 38.

At first, the age difference between me and my husband wasn't too bad, because I couldn't get it into my head that he was only the age he was. I used to cut his hair because I'm a hairdresser and I always thought he was a lot older than he was.

I was terrified of meeting his mother because I was so much older, plus the fact that I'd been married before and got two children. It had me worried. They live a very parochial life in Devon. But her attitude was, 'Oh! Thank goodness. Someone to look after him now.'

87

When I did first really realise how young he was, one half of me was saying, 'I can't do this, it's too undignified. I don't want anybody to know about this.' The other side of me went along with him and he was saying, 'I want you to take that part of your brain that thinks you're old and older than me. I want you to take it away. We get on so well. We love each other. It's got nothing to do with age.'

But of course the half of me that was sceptical would see how his young friends reacted to me. And the other half of me would ignore it. They had mixed reactions.

He told me that for three years he'd been in love with me. And he went back and told his colleagues that he was going to marry me one day. And that's just from talking to me in the salon. So he had all this foresight. And he had very short hair! Because he kept coming back all the time to get it cut. Every three weeks.

But it was shocking for me when I found my feelings seriously deepening. I had been on my own for a year and just thought, 'Oh well, we'll have a bit of fun here.' It had been really nice to be on my own after being married for 15 years. And then being with another man for four years who was *totally* wrong. So it was really nice having space and time and just getting to know myself really. In fact I'd got to the stage where I just thought, this is it now. I'm on my own for the rest of my life. I was only 38, but then to me that was quite old.

Then we did start going out together. And he said he wanted to get engaged. So I said, 'No. I don't want it to be that serious, because you're a young man.

You've got your life ahead of you. You'll want a family.' And I just kept him at bay. Because I just expected him to change.

Then time went on. And he said, 'I want you. Having a baby would be an added bonus. But it's not what I want to marry you for. I just want to be with you.' And so we went ahead and did it! And I was so shocked. I'd been to the gynaecologist because I'd just had some laser treatment for precancerous cells on my cervix, and I asked him what the chances are of having a baby. And much to my utter amazement and shock, he said, 'Go ahead. There's nothing wrong. You're fine.'

My GP was absolutely wonderful. She treated me like I was some special project. She liked the fact that I was happy with another man. It was almost as if I was taken under her wing. And then, of course, through the pregnancy, she thought I was absolutely fabulous because I had a good one. It was important to have her behind me. Though I wasn't singled out in particular, because of my age.

I had the amnio. I've worked with mentally handicapped adults. So I thought I probably would terminate. Because it's not so much the children. Everybody loves the children. Now whether I would have gone ahead with it, if it came to the crunch, I don't know. You see a little Down's baby or small child and they are the most loveable, adorable little things. And you want to give them all your care. But as they become bigger they are not so loveable. And nobody loves their child like you do. And if the chances are that you are older, you are not going to be around for a lot of their adult life. At the time when they're least attractive.

I have quite serious thoughts on having children. The fact that you are bringing a human being into the world. And you are responsible for that human being. I think that's really important. I don't say I've always felt like that. But as I've got older I have.

That's not something I thought about when younger. And is definitely a part of what being an older mother is about for me. The responsibility of bringing another human being into the world is *such* a *huge* thing. They're not 'objects' of a marriage or partnership.

Another consideration of feeling happy about having a child this late on in life had something to do with the fact that Tony was only young. He will be around maybe when I'm not. So the child will always have someone there.

We got married on 1 December 1990. And she was born nine months later. I was absolutely over the moon when she was conceived. I had wondered if I could have children.

Tony was completely knocked out. He had always said she would be a bonus. But that was a load of rubbish. He really wanted one. He's the sort of man who appreciates everything. He was *with* me. It was so great being with a more modern man. It was so thrilling watching his reactions.

My first husband was just so different. My ex-husband's 50 this year. So his attitude was very much ... 'Well, once you're pregnant, it's your business. Woman's business.' I don't think he found it particularly ugly. But he never told me it was attractive. He didn't like to feel the baby moving. Whereas Tony was just completely involved. He wasn't frightened of being involved. It wasn't any slight on his sexuality. Whereas the generation before have all these sort of hang-ups about being involved with women's things.

Tony was at the birth. It helped tremendously. It wasn't an easy birth. It was the hardest of all three. My muscles weren't the same and she was a bigger baby. Just being there and just being loving as he was, helped so much. And sharing it. I didn't have any drugs at all. He'd massage me. He'd walk me to the toilet. The last six hours were pretty tiring because I'd been up all night. It's sharing something of that depth that is the most incredible thing. And I am one for sharing. And he cut the cord. He gets very emotional.

He made me feel I'd done well. And I made him feel that he'd done well. Because the moment she was born, I said, 'Oooohhhhh! you've given me a *daughter*!' It was just totally wonderful.

Looking after her has been tiring. I think I'm feeling it more than I did when younger. But then I'm a lot more conscientious, I suppose, as an older mother. I'm aware of a lot more things. Like you realise children are very receptive under the age of three.

You know when you're older, there's no easy way. You've got to get up and do it. You've got to feed them. And change them and make sure they're comfortable. You're realistic as an older mother. Common sense in a way.

I would recommend having a baby later in life. The only thing I find frustrating in my life is the fact that I've already brought up a family, went back to work full time, got my independence and now I'm back to where I started. I had to battle to have a life after my first two kids and it was a lot to give up. I mind that a bit. I get bored. A bit of *déjà vu*. Here I am again. And your mind doesn't belong to yourself when you've got a small child. You have to divide it.

I can deal with the boredom thing though by putting on Radio 4 and doing something. And I go out a lot. I make sure we go to the library once a fortnight. And right from the beginning she's been to toddler groups.

Physically I don't think I could cope with another pregnancy and birth. I just haven't got the energy. I don't want anything to mess me up, to jeopardise my future with Alice.

Another thing about being an older mum, I've never let people pressure me. It would have been so easy to be pressured into taking maternity leave and going back to work. And I didn't want to do that. So when you get a bit older, you think, 'Right, this is the way I want to do it. And nobody's going to tell me otherwise.' Then you have the confidence to go ahead and do it. I'm *bringing* this human being into the world and they're going to get the best. I've got a very old-fashioned idea of having children I suppose.

Alice is so important to us. On Monday we went to a street party. And she was dancing around. She came running up to me and she said, 'Mummy I'm having a *lovely* time.' And I'd look at her and she was moving around just singing to herself and just watching everyone. And she was dancing and loving life. And it took me back to the Coronation. I was her age when it took place. And we had a big street party. And it reminded me of *me*. You know, dancing around. I never had that feeling with the boys. Alice has made all that fresh for me. It takes me back to when I was a child. I'm sure Tony and I would still be very close even without her, but every night when we kiss her goodnight, we sneak in together to make sure she's covered up, and he comes out and says, 'Isn't she lovely.' Often we'll say, 'We are *so* lucky.'

SINGLED OUT

However it works out, remarriage means a two-parent family. But in a survey by Ann Condy, for the Family Policy Studies Centre, we learn that children in fewer than 1 in 4 homes now have both parents living with them. The number of households containing the 'traditional' family unit, with parents either married or living together, has dropped from 32 per cent a decade ago to 24 per cent. Meanwhile, the number of one-parent families has almost tripled in the last two decades, from 8 per cent in 1971 to 22 per cent in 1993. That's almost 10 per cent of households nationwide, or a total of almost two million parents and children. And when you hear the phrase single, or lone, parent, in 91 per cent of cases that means lone *mother*. And how are they faring? Only 40 per cent of single mothers work, compared with 63 per cent of all mothers. Forty-six per cent have a weekly income of less than £100. Added to this, single parents are much more likely to live in council homes than other parents – 57 per cent compared with 17 per cent.

At the same time, a growing number of women are rejecting marriage: the number of single women aged 19 to 49 rose from 18 per cent to 28 per cent in the period 1979 to 1993. Twenty-two per cent of non-married women prefer to stay so by living with a partner rather than tying the knot, compared with half that figure in 1979. Many older mothers, over 40, fall into that last category. The number of women who are married has dropped from 74 per cent to 59 per cent.

Susan May Brown: Single Mother

I'm 43 now, and I've just stopped everything. I've stopped my social life. Completely. Then just last November I met a man who made me start having a social life again. I warned him: 'Don't come into my life if you're going to take away my contentment because I have a very simple life now and I'm very happy.'

We have a routine and we used to lie, Anna and me, on the sofa watching the TV and I would marvel at how happy I was. Isn't it a miracle that I don't feel that I should be doing something else. Or that I'm missing something.

I have a friend who's an incredibly successful businesswoman. She runs her own international company, is in her mid-forties, with no children. She has a suitor, but she's relaxed about not being in a relationship and is keeping him at arm's length. She doesn't actually think that I have a life. She thinks that real life is having complete control.

I had never meant to have a child. I had four little brothers. I felt I had raised my children. And I didn't want any children during my 10-year marriage. My husband didn't want them. I probably wasn't desperately in love with my husband. I met someone else and fell madly and passionately in love. I have a theory that when you fall in love like that, the hormones crank up.

I didn't use birth control with my husband. It was

kind of hit and miss, and I never got pregnant. I fell in love and immediately became fertile. And I started thinking about children all the time. I mean I would pass a pram and chase it down the street like a dog chases hubcaps. It was all I could think about. I was just consumed by it.

Having the baby was also, at that time in my life, about self-confidence. I didn't have any real self-confidence because I hadn't actually proven myself in any way. And I thought if I can have this baby on my own, then I will have proven to myself that I have the strength to do something.

The passionate relationship was over. And I had the baby all on my own. The father was on the sidelines. And I was really worried about it. Because I thought, what if I fail myself at the birth. I had decided to myself that I wanted to try to do it without any pain-killing drugs at all. In a way it would become a rite of passage.

So I got through it. There was such a feeling of triumph. Such a celebration. I felt now, I *know* I am strong enough to have this child, to raise this child on my own. It's silly. But the birth was symbolic. If I could do that, then I'd be all right as a mother. I knew I would have the stamina to raise this child on my own. It was my measure for myself. If I hadn't done it I don't know, I suppose there would have been the joy.

It was the most incredible joy. I suppose every mother feels that way. You just can't stop smiling and laughing. Taking me completely out of myself. And even though I didn't love the father any more I talked about it to him. He was the only other person in the world who could know, who could speak my language at that time.

That was the only thing that was even remotely sad or empty about it. That I didn't have anyone to share it with. It's like going to a funny film. And you can't relive it or discuss it later. There's no sharing. I wanted to do that.

I'd been working in a very classy national institution where you are considered lucky just to be given a job. It wasn't hard to give up, I couldn't bear to leave her. Plus I was breastfeeding her till she was two-and-a-half years old. Which I had to fight everybody about. My mother breastfed none of her children, so she couldn't see the point of it from the beginning. All my friends thought it was ridiculous. The truth is, they thought it was a bit vulgar. You know.

I never trusted anybody with her. I had one woman come, who I'd have there even when I was there, paying her with money I didn't have. She was all right. She was very gentle, very loving. And Anna still talks to her on the phone and stays in touch. That's so that she has other people in her life. Because all my family is in America.

The last four or five years, financially, it's been a disaster. A complete nightmare. There's just not enough money ever. And I couldn't send her to a state school. I looked at the one near here and I went over there and there were 30 kids in the classes. They didn't have the money, the time to teach them. The playground was like Vietnam. They were killing each other, and flying off the climbing frame overhead. I took her with me. And she crept closer and closer to me and said, 'The boys are so rough.' She went to this precious little nursery school with a spinster teacher, that I never liked. Now she's going to a small, private, progressive school, which I do.

In order to make ends meet, to manage, I sold everything. I sold all my jewellery. I sold furniture. I sold my antique quilt collection. I bought a collection of rare books, which are something I know about. I made up a catalogue and sold those on. I was lucky a couple of times. And I got through every penny that I saved. I was down to my last £100. But then I was able to sell the flat and made a big profit. I made £80,000. Used that to buy my current flat, every penny. So now I have no money again. No mortgage, but no money.

I asked the father for money for Anna. He'd disappeared out of her life for four years. Now he sees how fantastic she is, he's been trying to come back into our lives. He adores her, and really wants to be her father. In fact we went together to a child psychiatrist, who said don't tell the child yet. I wanted her to get to know him and to develop a relationship first. I didn't want to introduce her to a strange man and say, this is your father. Because of the expectations that it would put on both of them. The roles he'd have to play. The role she'd expected him to play. Or herself to play.

The bad thing is she doesn't see any point to him. She doesn't understand why he comes to the house. First of all, I said no toys. He's terribly rich. So I said to him, 'Absolutely you are not going to use that as leverage.' And he said, 'But I went to New York last week, and then I went to Hamleys.' And I said, 'It doesn't matter. Spend time with her. Do things that she thinks are fun.' Well, they had no common ground. There was nothing between them.

Now, I don't know if she's picking up something from me. He's not someone that I kiss hello and put

97

my arms around. He comes to see her obviously. And I think she's suspicious of that. What I hope ... I don't know what will happen. It doesn't matter how she feels about him, she's going to blame me for it. You know, 'Who is my father? Where has he been? Why did he go away? Did you push him away? How could you make such a stupid choice? Why would you let this man be my father? Why didn't you choose someone nice?'

Recently I asked him if he would pay half the school fees. And I got back a letter that had been dictated to his secretary in very legalistic tones outlining what the payments would be. He would pay half, but he would stretch it out in payments over the year, which does me no good this week, this month, this term. Suddenly because I've asked him to help, and he's said yes, he wants his money's worth. When I got the letter I burst into tears, and sobbed and sobbed because we had a bitter court battle to get him to pay any maintenance at all. I thought, 'Oh, God. I should never have let him come back. He never applied for visitation rights. He doesn't have any, and would have to go to court to get those. The only reason he is there, and the only reason he's come back is because I'm trying to uphold her rights. I'd like her to like him.'

He had left me stranded. He went off to Cap Ferat with his girlfriend. I was based in Paris, where I had the baby, and he bought a flat, and we were sitting there, and I had maintenance. But suddenly it all stopped. He told me to get out of the flat. Stopped the money. Everything. The whole time was fraught with anxiety and hatred and bitterness. And sadness and loss.

Being an older mother has made me feel completely isolated. I don't look my age so no one has said, 'Oh my God, you're too old to have this child, what are you thinking?' It never seemed unseemly. The fact I had her outside marriage was very difficult for a lot of people. What I found was that people I thought should support me, didn't.

I said to myself, This is the only important thing in my life. It's *the* only thing in my life actually of any value and I'm just having to go on instinct. And I did.

So anyway, I was late so I waited a couple of weeks. And I just thought, it can't be. I can't be pregnant. I had just moved in sharing with a girlfriend who was French, and I took the pregnancy test to her to read and she read it and she started to say, 'You must get an abortion.' I had only just moved in with her. She was very lonely. She had come out of a very unhappy marriage and was now a single woman trying to find her feet. We were very close friends, like sisters.

And I said, 'OK. We'll talk about it in the *morning*.' And I went back to deep sleep. I was awakened by a child's voice. It came from my stomach. And the voice said – I can never tell this story without crying – 'Mama, don't you love me?'

And I sat up in bed and I said, 'Yes! So now it's just you and me.' It was startling. So from that moment on there was no question that I would go through with it. I packed up all my things again.

The pregnancy was bliss. I never had any depression. I had fatigue. I never had any nausea. When I went into labour I went with a friend who's the daughter of a man well known in the alternative and complementary medicine scene. I thought it would be OK but it wasn't. She couldn't bear to see me in pain and started screaming for me to have drugs immediately, she couldn't bear to watch me hurting. I got up and went to the bathroom and I felt so alone. I remember putting my head on the sink and I was just sobbing.

But I had a wonderful midwife. And I kept saying to her, 'Don't call the doctor. We'll do this by ourselves.' And she said, 'I have to because we're in a hospital.' So the contractions went on, until I felt a very strong urge to sit up and as soon as I did the waters broke. And I felt the earth move. From up here at my sternum down to my pelvis. The whole body just went whhhumpphh!

Then it was time to push. And this low, lowing sound came out of me. The doctor had come and wanted to use forceps on the baby, and I knew I had to get her out, that he wasn't going to use those metal tweezer things on her. I remember looking over at the drip and there was blood in it. With the effort of pushing her out, I'd pushed the blood out of my arm back up the tube.

After we returned from hospital, the father insisted that we have this baby nurse at the cost of 300 to 400 pounds a week. Anna breastfed every 15 minutes round the clock. I just lay in bed with her all the time. We ate, and slept and ate and slept. Thank God I had the baby nurse to bring me food. I was so tired. That was the hardest part. But I was so alone. It made me stronger. If I'd had a husband there, or a mother, or someone who'd said this is not what you do, I don't know. The fact that I was alone made it much easier.

Being an older mother I think it was a better experience for me. I know it was a better experience for the child. I knew in my heart that her first impressions of life were going to be the most important. And I had to fight for that. That it be all right. That the world would not be terrible. I wanted only good things.

The biggest thing for me about being older was I didn't think any of this was detracting from any part of life. So many of my friends' husbands, when they were young, having babies would say, 'I'll be glad when we get back to life, a real life.' Not looking on their time with their young children as being the next part of their life, which was real, and might be permanent.

This child is not a temporary thing that has been inserted here. I embarked on this as if I were an exile to a new country. An exile of my own volition. That what I had left behind was something that I didn't have any need of any more. This was my new life. My new person. It's been the only important thing, the only significant thing to date in my life. Everything else pales.

I don't want her to be like me. I want her to be confident and capable and happy. I'm like all the rest of us. This is the new breed. I hope that she will have her own priorities and have enough confidence to stand up for them, and to make those priorities for life. I was pushed, and manipulated and led and put on paths, and when I look back I think I was the victim of my life. I want Anna to be the strong and the bold one. The carefree and the happy one. I want her to be the hero of her life.

THE BIGGER PICTURE

The picture drawn by the statistics we've seen so far in this chapter can be interpreted as one of gloom, or as an indicator of a healthy societal shake-up, depending on your viewpoint. Whatever your feelings about the demise of the traditional family unit, the signs do seem to point to a challenging time – both invigorating and uncertain – for women and for mothers.

While their choices of lifestyle may be expanding rapidly, the fact remains that nine-tenths of women in this country have children. Moreover, more of them than ever before are working, and fewer and fewer are doing that double shift out of choice. It is now an economic necessity. This enormous change in the conditions surrounding childbearing and rearing has happened without a concurrent revolution in childcare provision, or a change in school schedules.

As the FPSC report states, Britain comes around the bottom of the European league in terms of state nursery and childcare provision. Childcare, or the lack of it, is one of those benchmarks that you can use to measure how 'family-minded' a society is. Set alongside this are the claims of the counselling organisation, Relate, who say that the last decade has seen a huge increase in family breakdown, as well as psychological problems and stress. They are helping twice as many people as they did a decade ago. The absence of a 'feel-good' factor – how positive we feel about our lives, ourselves and the future – can, in fact, be one of the main reasons women delay or forgo having children. People in the former East Germany, for instance, who have suffered massive unemployment and the ending of state childcare since the fall of the Berlin Wall, have reportedly experienced a loss of faith in the future and this has been put down as one of the reasons they have one of the lowest birth rates in Europe.

So lack of childcare makes motherhood all the more daunting, particularly in a society where marital (and, one assumes, co-habitational) breakdown is amongst the highest in Europe. We live in a country that offers some of the poorest protections to a mother, both on a personal and on a public level.

Many mothers work full time, with their babies in nurseries, at childminders', or with nannies. Many more women are grateful for (insecure) part-time work, around which they fit family routines. This leaves them vulnerable at work, grossly underpaid, underpromoted and under-protected by employment law across all income groups, and whatever their job or career.

In this risky atmosphere, older women may be seen as less vulnerable than younger ones when it comes to starting a family. Having had more time to establish themselves at work and perhaps having tried and tested an enduring relationship, they may on the face of it seem better placed than the younger woman. But in some lines of work the older woman will be facing a dwindling marketability as the jobs go to younger and younger people. Then, too, women of all ages are faced with juggling home, children and work in an uncertain economic and social climate. It is hardly surprising that more and more women are delaying having their families – and in the process, becoming older mothers.

Though it's worth noting one interesting trend researched by Datamonitor that indicates the situation is clearly not precarious for all parents. They estimate that working mothers have fuelled a £2 billion baby boom in the high street, and say that it is the older mothers who are the most likely to splash out the fruits of their careers. Sales of baby goods have also increased – by 42.5 per cent since 1989, even though the birth rate has remained static. Baby clothing is the biggest money-spinner of the infant industry. That market alone was worth £610 million last year and has grown by more than 50 per cent since 1989, when it brought in £402 million. Baby foods, dominated by Heinz and Cow & Gate, were worth £317 million last year, compared with £191 million five years ago.

RIGHTS AND WRONGS

The statisticians and sociologists have provided a valuable body of data about older mothers in economic and social terms. But it remains nothing if not an emotive issue, stimulating some of the livelier debates one hears. Once something becomes a trend rather than a rarity, morality is brought into question – and it becomes the preserve of the pundits.

We'll have a look at what the latest pundits think about the issue; and afterwards, air the views on motherhood of the feminist philosophers whose opinions so many women use as touchstones in their lives. We may be in for a few surprises.

'The Moral Maze'
When it emerged that women are having fewer babies, and that the babies they *are* having are arriving later and later in their lives, the facts hit the media with a big splash. The pundits and commentators then engaged in much righteous tut-tutting. Where would it all end? Is the older mother capable? Is this any way to populate a healthy society? No article or programme seemed to capture the prevailing spirit of astonishment better than Michael

Buerk's 'The Moral Maze', on Radio 4. By examining the questions raised in the programme we begin to get an idea of how and why these particular changes in fertility patterns so unsettle people.

The debate was about fertility rates among women of all ages, but as we know, 'the older mother' now has her well-established niche among those statistics. Setting the agenda for the discussion Michael Buerk read:

A report this week based on projections from official census figures says 1 in 5 women in this generation will probably never have a child – double that of their mothers' generation. How much of this is voluntary choice, how much social and economic pressure, is an open question being hotly debated. The facts themselves are clear and their implications scarcely less so. The birth rate in the main childbearing age range is at its lowest since the darkest days of the Second World War... By 2011 there'll be more pensioners than children. Is it wrong? And if so, who's to blame? The feminists for confusing sexual equality with the right to live a man's kind of life? For judging success and fulfilment by male standards? Successive governments for discriminating against, rather than supporting, the family? Men for becoming less and less adequate and available as partners? Or women themselves? Do women have some sort of ethical responsibility to be mothers?

The thrust here was clearly the falling birth rate, but as we know, these figures also indicate that women are having their babies later. The unspoken subtext to this opening script is that, not only are there new choices available; the demographics are proving that women are exercising them. But – returning to the text itself – what is 'a man's kind of life'? The basic realities of men's lives are that they earn 25 per cent more than women and have less to lose when they have children. Working class women are stuck in female ghetto industries with poor pay. Middle class women hit glass ceilings. All of them just want equal pay and equal opportunities. There is no confusion.

Further, the script implies that if you are a woman who is beginning to question if, and also when, to have children, you are not only a 'feminist', you are ineluctably and inappropriately abrogating rights and freedoms that in the main belong to men. And so it goes on. But the real humdinger is asking whether women 'have some sort of ethical responsibility to be mothers'. It's as if they are saying, 'Come on gals, the birth rate in the rich white Western world is down. Damn global catastrophe and overcrowding, we're all going to be left penniless by an old age overcrowded with overly dependent geriatrics. Get cracking. Breed!'

The hunt was on, all right. And the 'mother' was the prey. And if not the mother, then the 'childless' (rather than 'child-free') woman. Many older mothers are, after all, child-free, for much of their adult life.

As is fitting in a programme about morality, the debaters spoke in general terms, with much philosophising. But Ceridwen Roberts of the Family Policy Studies Centre, whose research figures had sparked off the debate, had a number of specific points to make. She noted that it is not just the highly qualified middle-class woman who is delaying having her children. It's women across all classes. 'It's happening in ordinary families,' she said, 'where women are finding it difficult to put two incomes together and make a family life.'

She also cited as a reason for women delaying having their children that people generally 'have less and less experience of having children, with fewer siblings around, no cousins or extended families. The current generation of women actually don't know very much about babies.' Mrs Roberts commented, too, on the reasons women are reluctant to give up work. 'There are three good reasons,' she says. 'They have moved very dramatically away from the situation where there is an adequate breadwinner wage for men and support from the state for families with children . . . The other reason women don't give up work is we've given them an appetite for it. We've made them feel that if they don't have a working status they are good for nothing. Plus it's an insurance policy. They know what divorce is going to do.'

All very strong and salutary stuff. But what do the notorious 'feminists' themselves think?

Women beware women?
It is shocking to learn that many of our most respected feminist writer/philosophers have taken a very jaundiced view of motherhood *per se*. Going all the way back to one of the most important feminists of the late 18th century, Mary Wollstonecraft, we hear her saying in *Vindication of the Rights of Women* that mothers were fools and flirts who endangered their young in their pursuit of pleasure. 'The want of natural affection in many women, who are drawn from their duty by the admiration of men, and the ignorance of others, renders the infancy of man a much more perilous state than that of brutes.' Wollstonecraft hoped that better education would improve women's morals.

Time moves on, but it seems prejudices do not. Some 150 years later, Simone de Beauvoir decided that education wasn't enough. In *The Second Sex*, she says that mother-hood was to be avoided by any woman who sought 'authenticity'. Presumably, in her eyes, women who fulfilled their biological function in some way com-promised themselves, undermining their integrity as individuals. She goes on to describe women who enjoy pregnancy as 'not so much mothers as fertile organisms, like fowls with high egg production' who 'seek eagerly to sacrifice their liberty of action to the functioning of their flesh'.

Germaine Greer, clearly a champion of women the world over, surprises with some curious notions which slipped into her early influential work, *The Female Eunuch*. She talks about the archetype of Mother and says that 'our society is sick' because it 'insists on Mother's domination as a prerequisite for character formation. The child's attention must be weaned away from exterior reality onto an introverted relationship of mutual exploitation which will form the pattern of his future compulsions.' Mothers are seen as inevitably drawn into a relationship with their children which will warp and destroy their capacity for healthy psychological growth.

Here, yet again, and this time from within the feminist fold, may be another reason why women perhaps delay – even choose never to engage in – having children: if the very women who champion women think this way, where does that leave the rest of us?

AN EYE TO THE FUTURE

Out of the mouths of babes
One group whose lives we haven't yet considered is that of younger women. While a discussion centred on them may seem out of place in a book on older mothers, the fact

is that many of them are the mothers of the future. A look at their choices now can tell us a great deal about whether current trends are likely to continue.

A new survey, *It's A Woman's World – Youth Lifestyles 1995*, seems to indicate that the 'rebellious' streak so many older women are supposed to be exhibiting by having their children late is apparent across the generations.

Carried out by Mintel, the survey shows that young women are facing the future with more confidence and less conformity than their male peers. Women aged 15 to 24, inspired by better job opportunities and educational success, are more likely than young men of the same age to want to travel and see the world before launching their careers. Young men appeared more alarmed than women by the prospect of life without a steady relationship. The women were more concerned with developing platonic friendships.

There seemed to be less conformism among women in their late teens, with 4 in 10 saying they reject their parents' lifestyles. Less than 30 per cent of their male peers took a similar stance.

Mintel are not the only organisation studying young women. The Family Policy Studies Centre has recently reported that 1 young woman in 5 these days does not have children, compared with only 1 in 10 women from her mother's generation. They go on to surmise that an increasing proportion of women are choosing to be childless and projections suggest that 20 per cent of women born in the 1960s, 1970s and 1980s will never have children.

Futurologists are, however, notorious for getting things wrong. What I would hazard as a guess for the future is that many of these young women actually will have children, but much later in their lives. I would suggest that motherhood is now a far more moveable feast than it used to be. As many older mothers know, the instinct to have children can lie dormant for many a year and it is for some only the increasingly loud ticking of that biological clock that kickstarts the late onset, but nonetheless urgent imperative, to get on with it.

Michaela Strachan, presenter of the BBC wildlife programme *The Really Wild Show* and children's television veteran, seems to uphold both the findings of the FPSC and my hunches. At 28, she says,

> At the moment I just can't imagine having children. I enjoy my life so much as it is that I don't want to change my lifestyle.
>
> Admittedly, it's a very natural thing to want to have children. But we don't live a natural life any more and these days women have to work. Having a child is an enormous decision and I believe a lot of women don't think about it hard enough beforehand.
>
> It does run through my mind that I might get to 40 and wish I'd had children. Maybe I'll reassess the situation when I get to around 36, or find my hormones change my mind for me.

Whither the family?

With so many young women now delaying having children, along with so many older ones, and with so many couples divorcing or choosing not to marry in the first place – in short, with so many extreme shifts going on around us – can we predict anything of the future?

There is a school of historical thought called pendulum theory, which claims that societies undergo swings between conventional and radical behaviour at regular intervals. According to this model, we'll revert to traditional family units all too soon, and the excesses of the present will be history.

This theory may begin to break down, however, when we learn how much remains constant in society even through a myriad apparent changes. The strict moral probity of the Victorian era, for instance, hardly put paid to sex: there was a virtual epidemic of syphilis at the time. And today, the 'dissolution' of the family may be a fantasy. Among the wealth of research I studied, I came across this statement: 'It is thought that around 3 of every 4 births outside marriage in 1993 took place within stable relationships.' So it seems, perhaps, that a family unit is after all still seen as vital for child rearing by most parents.

What does seem to be changing is when we choose to set up our oases of stability: and that is, as we've seen, later and later. For the rest, it becomes difficult to foresee what the next millennium holds. Some futurologists suggest survival strategies for people in the 21st century. Their implications are chilling, but better, perhaps, to be forewarned and forearmed.

They advocate facing up to the prevalence – and thus the probability – of divorce and separation, and learning to separate without fighting, as it is that which seems to do the most damage to children. For the same reason they warn parents to be careful what they teach young children about family life. Don't encourage them to think that mummy and daddy will always be together.

If you are a woman, abandon the idea that you will have a man to lean on. It is highly likely that you will be your family's sole breadwinner at some point. If you are a man, become a New Man, or women will spurn you. (And remember: equal work means equal, not token.) Finally, campaign and lobby for employers to give women equal pay, and for the government to finance childcare.

It's hard school. But these maxims from the futurologists have a ring of truth about them, and many live by them already. For women who have taken them on board as 'survival strategies', these simple truths may very well affect their decisions about when to have children. If a woman waits till later, she may have a more established and dependable relationship. Or, if she doesn't have that, she may have a more established and dependable career. Happily, she may have both. But whatever her situation she would be better prepared practically and materially for parenting.

Conspicuous by his absence in all this is the father. No one has been asking men questions or studying them as closely as they have women. 'We particularly need to know what men think about having children. There's virtually no research on it,' says Ann Condy, who's currently starting a study on exactly that.

Musing about the future is endlessly fascinating. But meanwhile, older mothers are simply getting on with the task in hand. We'll be looking at the experiences of a number of them next in the 'Second Trimester'.

SECOND
TRIMESTER

As we've seen, women become mothers in their late thirties, their forties, even their fifties, for a vast array of reasons. Here we explore three of the most frequent: infertility and other medical problems, delays in finding the right partner, and that classic – the eleventh-hour, fortuitous surprise.

CHAPTER 4

Touch and Go:

When the Body Falters

All of the women whose stories follow tried for a child for years. Some, like the actress Patricia Hodge, suffered from unexplained infertility. Some experienced a heart-breaking run of miscarriages. Others had their first children easily and relatively early, but were unable to complete their families until later, for a variety of medical reasons. What they all share is a profound determination to carry on, no matter how apparently hopeless their case.

Patricia Hodge: Actress, Mother

I always assumed I'd have children, absolutely, without a shadow of a doubt. I was always pas-sionately interested in children. When I was little, on a Saturday morning, I used to ring up my parents' friends that I knew had babies and ask if I could take their baby for a walk. I would always look after the little sister or brother of my older sister's friends. It had always been part of the scheme of things. But I was then fortunate enough to go into the profession I

115

wanted to. I didn't believe it would really happen, and then it did.

And of course, as with any vocational job, you really have to give it 100 per cent. I started acting fairly late. I didn't go to drama school till I was 22 because I trained to be a teacher first. That's because everybody said, Don't be silly, you're not going to be an actress. So I did a job that would mean working with children.

So I was over 24 before I got into the profession and was earning money. Then I had to give it a few years to build up. I married Peter when I was 29 and really it was from that moment that we assumed we would have children. I didn't get into any kind of even a query situation about fertility until I was about 35. I very tentatively went to see somebody and asked if I should investigate why nothing seemed to be happening for us. And I was sent away for a year to take my temperature, which was ludicrous. You do that if you're trying to avoid getting pregnant. Or if someone has been trying for six months. We'd been trying, albeit in a casual way, for six years.

My age crept up to 37. Then I started to see people who were seriously in the infertility business. I was comprehensively investigated. I think I've ended up having six laparoscopies in my life, so all of that went on. It was what they call unexplained infertility. Which of course is the biggest cause. If you can put your finger on something specific then it's a help, because perhaps they can then do something about it. I had IVF several times, but it came to nothing.

By now I was getting to 39 or 40. By the time I got to 41 I just began to despair. I went into a very, very difficult part of my life. It brought about a kind of depression that wouldn't have shown itself to the outside world. I just had no idea what the future would hold. I couldn't possibly have sat down and made plans, just because it seemed as if I was never going to have children. I went into a kind of frozen state, that's the only way I can describe it. Not able to address the issue of life at all. I just kept busy with work and I went in the direction I was pointed. But I couldn't effect anything for myself and I certainly couldn't go through any more clinical trials.

There is only one way that I can describe the whole experience. It is like grieving for the death of something you never had in the first place. These primeval instincts, in our highly sophisticated society, are very, very difficult to describe. You can't say why you want children.

I have complete regard for a woman who quite categorically knows she doesn't wish to have children. Or similarly, one who thought well, maybe I will, maybe I won't and in the end decides not to. I think it's a very clear, brave decision. It doesn't matter what you do in life as long as you're true to yourself.

But similarly, somebody who has that absolute calling to bring children into the world and to bring them up – let's face it, it's the hardest work we do. It's just as difficult, and some would say more so, to spend your time at home all day with young children as to work. Particularly when you get older, because your stamina and all your focus are very different from those of a young woman. It isn't the easy option. But if you do want to have children it is because you want to live life for someone else. You don't want to go on living it for yourself.

I couldn't begin to tell you what turned it around for me. Or why my body suddenly decided to click into action. Some years later my gynaecologist said to me that sometimes you can get everything apparently functioning normally, because so much is controlled by the clock of the pituitary gland, for example, but just one thing may be one degree out of kilter. For whatever reason, it may be an emotional block or it may be simply a metabolic problem. But everything is just 'out'. Once it clicks back, then everything works.

That was his explanation that I was then able to go on and have more. Because once the body had got into the right mode, it can do it. But what triggers it, what turns you around? Well, maybe, it's the release of some other focus. And I can only say that in my life, my father became terminally ill. I wanted to help and look after him and it was during that time that I actually got pregnant, completely naturally. It could be that something happened to me in that way. How will I ever know. I'm just very thankful that it did.

I was stunned when it happened. I could hardly believe it. I think at the moment that I was told, I didn't cry because I was completely shellshocked. Then of course you go through the next nine months thinking every day, 'I'm going to lose it.' I had an amnio for both pregnancies. It's a difficult decision to make. But knowing the odds, I think when I was 42 it was around 1 in 50. When I was 45 they were down to about 1 in 38. So there was really no question. I have a friend who I adore. He says, 'Why are we all in the business of wanting to bring perfect babies into the world?' Well, that's an important question. But my reasoning for having an amnio was not because I feared my child wouldn't be perfect. It was because, if a child isn't perfect, if it's going to have a major handicap, like Down's syndrome, in 20 years' time, if something happens to me, who is going to look after this child?

The pregnancies for me were fine. My doctor said as far as the age thing was concerned, that I would have no difference between my pregnancy and the pregnancy of a 21-year-old. He'd say that about anyone. And he's a pretty eminent chap. He says that the body, in reproductive terms, when 40, can carry a child as easily as it would have 20 years earlier. The difference is in the quality of the eggs. And the genetic structure. A girl of 21 is just as likely to develop pre-eclampsia as a woman of 41. You're just up for it like everyone else.

The births were pretty normal. Though my obstetrician knew how precious these babies were. That the chances, if anything had gone wrong, of my being able to say, well, I'll have another baby next year, were nil. So a deal of care was taken on that front. Therefore we made no pronouncements about whether the child would be born naturally, or by Caesarean or whatever, until we got right up to the starting post.

And I did actually get pre-eclampsia at the last minute, five weeks before the first baby was born. They decided to take me in and rest me for 48 hours and if it hadn't gone down they would have had to deliver me early. But it did go down. Then it shot up again about four weeks later. But then I was only a week from the date my obstetrician had set to induce me, if I hadn't gone into spontaneous labour before. He wasn't prepared to let me hang about.

He said to me the night before he planned to induce me that there was no evidence that I wouldn't give birth normally. But he also said he wasn't going to let it be a long protracted labour. So he induced me at eight o'clock in the morning. But I had no dilation. I had massive contractions, which were wonderful, but the dilation was going to take another 24 hours. So by three o'clock in the afternoon, he decided to get the epidural in, just in case.

All I had stipulated was that I didn't want to have a general anaesthetic. I didn't want to be knocked out. Then, at about half four that afternoon, he gave me a final examination and I had dilated just half a centimetre. 'We'll all be here at this time tomorrow,' he said and decided to go ahead with the Caesarean. I didn't care. I just wanted a safe delivery. So they turned the whole place into an operating theatre in the space of a quarter of an hour and I watched my son being born, which was just amazing.

The second time around he said categorically that I must have a Caesarean, because of the scar on the womb. They were two incredibly tranquil births. It's a wonderful way to give birth. You feel nothing. There's just this sensation of somebody rummaging around in a bottom drawer. My obstetrician and I just chatted away. Then he'd say, this noise you hear like a hoover, I'm just vacuuming out the amniotic fluid. And then suddenly they said, do you want to watch your baby being born and they lift the baby out of your tummy. It's quite magical.

As regards being an older mother, I think there is nothing more boring in the world than people walking around saying they're tired all the time. I've been enormously guilty of it at different times in my life. When I look back, as a 23-year-old drama student I used to say, 'I'm exhausted' because you think you are. I would simply say, as somebody said to me before I had my children, you don't know the meaning of tiredness till you have children. When you can't ever put your head on the pillow at night, and know that you're going to get a full night's sleep. If there is something wrong when they're little babies, it's like sleep deprivation torture. Being woken up just as you've drifted off.

In somebody older, you're not going to be as resilient. You can't pick yourself up the next day and walk round with a load of energy if you've only had two-and-a-half hours sleep. I went into rehearsal once and said, 'I've had two-and-a-half hours sleep. *Not* consecutively.'

That's because I chose to run a career along with my life. I think it's testing on all fronts being an older mother. In that also, of course, you are a different person. You've come a lot further down the proverbial road of life. On the good side, you know so much more about yourself. You've come to terms with all the ghastly things that are wrong with you and hopefully cashed in on some of the things that are right for you. And you're not trying to prove anything in the same way. So you can give a terrific dimension to children in those terms.

On the down side, you are not going to have such a carefree attitude to it all. I can't easily allow my child to just be walked across the road by somebody else. Their standards may not be the same as mine. I will always question, if my child is going in somebody's car, what the car is, and if there are seatbelts. One shouldn't deny those indicators of one's life experience. Experience has taught us to know that things do go wrong.

As a race we're all guilty of letting our heads rule our instincts. The truth of it is, it is much simpler than you allow it to be. That's really the lesson I've learnt. One worries like mad. Am I feeding for *exactly* the right time? Have they had *exactly* seven ounces of milk? You have to be able to let go. And just allow the child to take what it needs. If you just nudge it in the right direction, if you teach it to go off to sleep on its own, that is what it will do.

I have undoubtedly made a different mother as an older woman, than I would have done as a younger woman. I don't think that my values would have been different. I think I'm probably the mother I always would have been in terms of ethics and the way I feel life should be lived. But I think I'm probably wiser on a lot of fronts. And I think I may have found it more conflicting if I'd had them when very young. If I hadn't gone into the theatre and if I'd married at 21, 22, and had children then, I think I would have been frustrated by only doing that.

I do combine work and motherhood now, but actually, to be honest, I'm very lucky. I live in a freelance world, so I can to a certain extent be very selective. The truth of it is that I probably, on average, work half of the year. So I'm able to have periods of time when I work pretty hard, and then time when I'm a housewife and a mother.

I think the continuing of the profession is good nourishment for the soul. You have to learn to feed yourself as a human being, you must never let anything sap you dry. Because then you've got nothing to give. You've got to be the proverbial mother bird who's feeding herself with the worms, as well as carrying them back to give to her children. It's all part of the life experience. Just be truthful, really. And if that's the woman I always was, why should I pretend to my children to be something different?

I thank God every day that this happened to me. For better or worse I know it was the right path for me. Even at my lowest, tiredest, most distraught I would never turn the clock back and be without them.

It's a dimension that you know you have to go for. I do know that this has made me a far better person. It has brought about a sort of understanding of life and put me in touch with life in a way that I needed.

Shirley Blyth: Public Relations Consultant, Mother

I first got pregnant when I was 41 but I lost the baby at three months. I think I was fairly philosophical about that because I went to have a scan and it was what they call a blighted ovum. Which means some cells have divided, but then it stops. So there was nothing there. I felt disappointed, but I didn't feel a sense of loss. There was no way it was ever going to be viable. But having said that, three months is a long time to think you're pregnant, and then not be.

I think I probably would have been less philosophical if I had known it would take me another nearly three years to get pregnant again.

That's what people don't realise. I didn't have a baby so late by choice. Though having said that, I suppose in a way it was . . . because if I had really wanted to have one before, I could have got myself pregnant one way or another. But I decided that, although I'd like a child, it wasn't the be-all and end-all.

When I finally got pregnant again I must have been 44. I'd been on Clomid, a very mild fertility drug that makes you ovulate. It doesn't do anything else. It increases your chances of twins perhaps; that's it. But I said to my consultant, 'This isn't working, we can't go on "performing" to rote like this, it's affecting our love life.' So Chris and I said, if it doesn't work by Christmas, it's very sad, but it's fate and that's it. We'll give up on it. We've got such a good relationship, let's just enjoy that.

I went to see the consultant again in the May and then by June I'd conceived! Still taking the Clomid, but only giving it a few more months. And I'm sure being relaxed about it may help. I had tests. My husband had tests and we were both absolutely fine. I had a laparoscopy [the insertion of a fibre-optic camera to check the whole of the reproductive system]. But as my consultant said, 'At your age things don't always gel. We don't know why. Your eggs are obviously older, but we just don't know.' He said keep trying, but there was nothing more he could do really. He thought I was really a bit old for IVF. Though I didn't want to do IVF anyway; what people don't realise is that only 20 to 30 per cent of IVF works. There is debate about whether women over 40 should be given IVF at all.

Personally I think they should have the opportunity, but perhaps what these women don't realise is that at that age your chances of it being successful are less. If you've got the choice, you should have your babies before you're 40 if you can, simply because what you don't realise is that you may be functioning perfectly well but for some reason you just don't conceive right away. If you wait, you may have all sorts of problems, and then you've got no leeway. I conceived very quickly the first time, at 41, and then *nothing*.

One of the advantages of being older is that you can see all too clearly the good and the bad about having a child. We could see firsthand, from relations, how it does change your life. There are negative aspects. Your whole lifestyle changes. Having said that, having such a marvellous husband, I knew I still wanted one. Though I think we'd almost come to terms with how we possibly wouldn't have one.

And then it happened.

But this time, when I did conceive I was very cautious. I was absolutely thrilled. But what I asked for was that I have a very early scan to check that there really was something there this time. So I had it at eight weeks, the earliest you can. And there was . . . the Bean. That is a marvellous moment. But still for me, almost unreal. Because I think, to be quite honest, at this age you do have the fear that something is going to be wrong with the child. We tried to keep the whole thing quiet until we were absolutely sure.

It wasn't for religious grounds, or moral grounds. But I would have hated to make the decision if something had been wrong. I'm just very relieved we didn't have to. When I had the amnio, because my placenta was on the front, we had to have three goes at it.

A bit traumatic really. By then I'd had three scans. But all they could do with the scan is to say they can't guarantee that your baby hasn't got Down's syndrome, or whatever, but looking at it they say, we can see this, and we can see that and on the whole it looks good. I was amazed. They can see that the organs are formed. The head and the brain look fine, they said. There's no deposit at the back of the neck, which can possibly be a Down's thing. So you're 90 per cent of the way there. But they had to do the amnio as a surer thing.

That's when I got really excited. But I was still on this holding-back thing. When I had the amnio I wasn't worried about the harm to the baby. I had a very good consultant. They had him up on the screen, so they knew exactly where to do it. And as I said, I went back three times, because they couldn't get a window to get in and they wouldn't take a risk. They decided to wait till the baby moved. That was the bit I found traumatic. Because what happens then, it gets later and later.

The actual amnio itself was quite hard too. The needle was suddenly jabbed in. I felt this contraction. And I had a terrible fright. Chris was there, and I went, 'Ooooooohhh!', and Chris went, 'Uuuuuhhhhh!' and so did the radiologist. It was the consultant who was quite calm. That must have been the way he felt he had to do it, but I found that difficult.

But then the best thing of all was that, as I'd had it done privately, I had the results in the shortest possible time, about ten days. When he rang up he got to my husband, but he wanted to give me the news. And when he told me everything was all right, *that* was the moment that was so marvellous.

We'd decided that if everything was all right we wanted to know the sex. So we were told it was a boy. And *that* was a sense of euphoria. But I still felt, 'Goodness, is this real?' You get on to a different level. Inevitably I was thrilled, but I was trying to be very protective at the same time. We had made a decision that if something was wrong we would terminate. I think if we had to do that I'd have felt guilty. But I'm afraid we'd made that decision. If there was something wrong with the child I know that if I'd had the baby then I would have wanted to bring it up myself.

Very selfishly, I thought I didn't want to put myself in the position of having to do that. Getting married so late, I wanted to enjoy our relationship. I don't know. It would have been an agony for me. Whatever one does. It's just the most awful thing you ever have to do. Especially at that stage. I was a good five months pregnant.

So that's the down side, being an older mother. You could have problems with the child. Over 40, the statistics shoot up, and then again over 45.

The pregnancy itself was very good. I didn't get any morning sickness as such. If I felt queasy I just ate something, and it always went away for me. I didn't do special exercises. Maybe it was because I was advised to have a Caesarean. That gave me a slight cop-out.

I went to one antenatal class and it was dreadful. It was a midwife who was talking about one of her ladies who'd just had her first baby and how it had all gone so easily. Naturally, we were all delighted for this woman. But most people in the class were terrified and didn't want to hear about this stranger who'd done so terribly well, giving birth standing up and so on. The feeling I got was that if you wanted to do natural childbirth that was fine. But if you wanted to have an epidural or whatever . . . this midwife wasn't too hot on it. She didn't actively say she wasn't recommending it. She said, 'Only you can decide.' She said it's so much down to luck. For instance, you can be very fit and you can be young, but if the baby comes down at the wrong slant and you don't dilate properly, you can have a very long, very painful labour. Which obviously you don't plan. For other people it can happen quite happily. You know, popping peas is what they always say.

I kept very quiet, thinking, here am I having an elective Caesarean. I think I'll just sneak out now, while I'm ahead. You know, my high-tech bit. If I was younger, and this wasn't literally a 'last chance saloon' situation, maybe I would have had a 'natural' delivery. But my consultant was very good. He said, 'Look, it's up to you, but as you've had such trouble getting pregnant, and this is going to be your only one, I'd recommend a Caesarean.' These days it's safer for mother and baby. The baby doesn't have the trauma of coming down the birth canal.

Jack was over eight pounds when he was born. I was very lucky. I had it done privately. BUPA helped. BUPA doesn't pay as much as they used to towards pregnancy, but it was something. For me it was a pretty good experience.

I had an epidural because I wanted to be awake all the time. You're in an operating theatre. There were about 12 people, but they're chatting away, so it's a good atmosphere. We were all in stitches because my husband's so tall they couldn't find Wellingtons to fit his feet. So he said, 'I hope I don't keel over with lack of circulation wearing these small boots.' Everyone was laughing.

And it's like having a big tooth pulled. What people don't tell you is that although it doesn't hurt, you can *feel* the sensation. And I kept saying, 'No, I can still feel.' And I reckon they gave me a little too much epidural in the end. Because my *face* started to go numb. And one arm went a bit limp, which was a nuisance because when I wanted to hold Jack it was a bit difficult.

There's a screen up and you can watch as little, or as much as you like. I didn't watch any of the bit down there because I knew what they would be doing, and it's a bit gory. But Chris was there. When they lift the baby out you hear it crying. They quickly wipe away all the liquid and then you're holding it right away. So you do get that same wonderful sensation and that of course is the most extraordinary feeling in the world. You can't believe it. And nobody could believe how big he was. Long, long baby.

Every experience is different. Part of me would have liked almost the challenge of doing a more natural birth. But, in the end, I thought if that's what my consultant recommends . . . it's taken me 44 years to get to this stage. Let's get it right now.

Overall I think my pregnancy was very good, very easy. With my own business, I could set my pace a bit. I have to say these women that are working very much full time under pressure . . . travelling in and doing your 12 hours a day . . . I think I would have found that very difficult to do and I would have got overtired.

There's this awful pressure on women now to work up to the last minute. And it's silly. Of course you can still work. But if you carry on working at the pace that maybe you're used to then you get overtired. One friend of mine got seriously depressed and felt she couldn't cope. And there were others who chose to work to the last minute, had their babies and went back to work within a couple of weeks. And I think, well, *why?*

And with my Caesarean I was very lucky. It's a major op. So you do have to recover from it. They get you out of bed very quickly. And I had no problems with my stitches at all. I was walking around within a day, though slowly. But some women can have a very tough time. I know two other friends who've had really difficult deliveries. Both younger. One in her mid-thirties, the other 31. They've both had to go back and be stitched up again. One had a swab left in. The other was just back in last week. And her baby is 13 months old! She had to be restitched after a messy episiotomy. It's a scandal.

So I count myself very lucky because I had the high-tech bit, and yes of course there's trauma, but my recovery was very good. I breastfed probably for about two months. I had to top Jack up with a bottle from time to time, but I didn't mind that. I just wanted to breastfeed for the experience. And I think it is important that you at least try and even if you do it for a short while it's better than nothing.

Looking after him and working has been difficult. I think most people find trying to get that balance quite difficult. I had a client who I kept during the pregnancy and through the birth and while I was on maternity leave. I had someone else working on that account. I found that quite hard. Because the client remained demanding throughout. They wanted me to be on tap, even though they weren't paying to have me full time. So just when I thought, I've done this or that task and now I can look after the baby this afternoon, they'd ring and have to have something done then and there. And that would drive me crazy.

There were times when I had to put him in his playpen and of course he'd be screaming, and I'd be trying to do something on the phone. And I thought, I don't want to do this to him. It's not fair on him. It's certainly not fair on me. I couldn't tell the client about it. I just had to be professional. They weren't interested. Why should they be.

The main problem is getting help – if you don't want full-time help. I had always thought I wanted a full-time, live-in nanny, and then I realised I didn't want someone to take over my child, which they do inevitably. They grow up so quickly. I didn't want someone who was going to be with him 10 hours a day. For instance, even now, his nanny has taken him off shopping and then to the park, and I think, well, I'd like to sit with him in the park . . . it's a beautiful day.

I think I would have found it very hard to be an absolutely full-time mother. I'm sure that I appreciate the time with Jack, and appreciate the time with my work. We did have all sorts of problems getting the right help. We're fine at the moment because we do a nanny share.

There's this phrase, 'having it all'. I think for the older woman, if she's able to juggle work and a child she's lucky. Maybe she just decides to have a few years off to have the child, and then go back. You can only do that if you're established in your career, that's the trouble.

Working itself is manageable. My line is that I've had a baby, not a lobotomy. I know if I can sit down and have peace and concentrate, my brain is as keen as it ever was. But I do think getting down to concentrate is more difficult. Specially if you work from home. Your priorities change. But when I've had to do some presentations lately, if I can just shut the office door it's fine.

But they also jumped to all sorts of conclusions. That you're going to continue with your career as it is, or you're going to give it up totally. And they don't seem to realise that there is a half-way house. Because if you say 'part-time work' to anyone, they think this isn't serious work. There's a terrible prejudice about that. When you're working with clients who have this typical corporate structure in a commercial company, most of the men are married, with wives who are full-time mothers at home. So they don't know any different. But they're not quite sure about women who have children and do work, but not all the time.

I whizzed into the local paper shop recently and while looking through things, bumped into a next-door neighbour. She's very much a full-time mother, with her two children. And I suppose it's true, I never see her without them. But she looked at me and she said almost accusingly, *'Where's Jack?'* Like, 'How can you be here without your child?' It was surprise and almost resentment. In fact he was at home with my husband. I was just thinking how lucky I am. I could go out, and leave the baby quite happily. And of course if you're alone with the baby, you can't.

It is totally frustrating that whatever I *do* want to do, if I'm looking after Jack I can't do anything else. You just have to set your mind to it. You just have to take time. And whether it's doing mundane household tasks, and even that's difficult. You know, putting on the washing: 'No thank you Jack, no, I want to put it *in* the machine, not *out*.' But that's what

132

every mother has to contend with. You can't dry your hair because the hairdryer sets him off. Those sorts of things. Now if I had to deal with that all the time . . .

But none of this would be as good as it is without my husband. And I think having good support in that area is vital. I don't know how unusual we are. Most husbands now do take part in looking after the baby. And more and more of them share. Having said that, most husbands go out to work at a set time every morning and come back late at night. Which I think is a shame because they don't take part in bringing up the baby in the same way. Chris and I both have our own businesses and both have an office at home now. I lead on looking after Jack. I organise the food and the marketing because Chris works full time and I try and work part time. He does look after him though. And even during the day, if suddenly I've got an appointment and we haven't got the nanny, I can ask for him to take over. We take it in turns. Chris is as good with the baby as I am. And that is not only marvellous for Jack, because it doesn't mean he has to go to Mummy, I think it's very rewarding for the man.

I think as a working woman you're used to being independent and it's been often quite tough. You've been struggling in my case to get out of being a secretary. So you gain an executive position. Then you gain a team. Then you're used to perhaps being the only woman in the boardroom as a consultant, as I was. You get used to that. And you've earned it. You enjoy it.

But, you know there's another side to life and you want that too. But to give it all up completely. Very difficult. I see this as a lovely sabbatical. I was asking about nursery school recently and I thought, 'God! In another two years he'll be at nursery school!' This is frightening. His father is very involved with him. We have a wonderful relationship. You suddenly realise you've found the gem. The treasure. I just threw my prejudices out of the window. And I thought, this is *right*. So inevitably trying to have a child followed. But it wasn't straightaway. We were living together for a while, and I didn't even get rid of the coil till we were married. I said, 'We're not going to rush, now.' Little did I realise ... That's the thing with older women. I think if older women are looking for Mr Right, they won't find him, they'll frighten him off. It's like you carry a brand on your forehead. I think you just have to go with it and enjoy life for what it is.

Rosi Harkin: Housewife

I was 38 with my first pregnancy. I'd thought it would take me ages to conceive, but when I stopped the Pill I became pregnant straightaway! Which was wonderful.

I had an amnio and everything was fine. It never occurred to me to worry. I don't remember being anxious about what the results were going to be. It was just something we had to do because we couldn't have coped with a disabled child, so we had to know. A healthy child was going to be shock enough at our age.

Max was born prematurely but he was perfectly healthy at 35 weeks. Though he had a club-foot. That was difficult, I suppose, because we all expect our children to be perfect. I reckon that's why he came early, because he needed something done about that. It's been rectified and he's fine now after various bits of surgery. It doesn't stop him doing anything.

It was some years before we decided that we would have any more. Max was not difficult, he was wonderful. I suppose . . . being of a Catholic up-bringing and Catholic background . . . and Mike and I are not married . . . I felt that one child outside marriage was OK in the 'sin' stakes, but two were pushing it! It's all in your subconscious. It's all there.

That's why we waited so long before we tried again! And I always maintain, as well, that the longer the gap the better, because children are children for so little time. It's very difficult to ask a two-year-old to grow up because you've got a baby.

So I was about 40 before we decided we'd try again, and it took quite a while this time, about a year. That surprised me. Although people are having babies much later, I don't think most women are aware that although we may feel like someone in our twenties, the reality is that our fertility does not go on forever. Simply physiologically, your eggs have been there since you were born. Things start to disintegrate.

But, I did get pregnant again. Mike, who writes software, got a temporary job for six weeks on the Isle of Man. So we decided to all go there for the summer. We'd taken a house and it was going to be fun, that last year before the baby arrived. And there again I had to go and ask for an amnio.

I was by then about 16 weeks pregnant. I'd just done the pregnancy test myself. So finally we managed to get an amnio organised at a hospital on the Isle of Man and when they were doing the test I

135

discovered that termination is actually illegal there.

I suppose about three weeks passed. And I was more anxious this time, for no apparent reason. I think it came from the fact that I had more knowledge the second time around. About how hazardous it is the older you get. But I was thinking about Down's syndrome. I think I rang the hospital and they said the spina bifida check had come out all right. But they didn't have the chromosome count. They were hedging their bets, and they wouldn't tell me. Finally they rang Mike at work and said that we needed to go in for an appointment, because we needed to discuss the results and I suppose we sort of knew. But when we got to the hospital, they treated us like eggshells and we were put in a special room. Our apprehension rose, the kinder people were to us.

So this doctor came in and said, 'Well I'm afraid, as you have probably suspected . . . ' And I *hadn't* expected . . . I didn't really want them to find anything. My baby had Edwards' Syndrome. Which is three of chromosome 18, instead of two. It wasn't Down's at all. My baby would have lived a week, perhaps two weeks, possibly not longer than six months and would have been very handicapped. Lungs. Heart. Facial defects. Deformities.

The doctor was very kind. So we asked, well what happens now, as abortion is illegal here? But he'd been in touch with the medical council's Board of Governors for the Island and they were prepared to allow the termination to be carried out there.

It was just a matter of steeling yourself to do it really. We went for a walk on the beach and cried a lot. It was like a bad dream. I felt I was going to wake up and it was going to be all right. This wasn't real.

There was no way we were going to allow our child to die slowly. I mean, I may not even have gone full term. Something may have happened before then. So. This child was going to die. It was a question of when. Whether I was going to pre-empt it and stop it *now*. Or I was going to allow it, allow *her*, to carry on and . . . have pain. You just don't know. But to have a week's life . . . or whatever. It was horrible.

Mike cried after she was born. And I'd never seen him cry, before then, or since. And he just wept, because of the waste. The potential for life that was there. But yet wasn't there. And he's not particularly religious. And probably thought, 'That *bastard* God, if there is a God.' Anger and sadness.

At 20 weeks you have to actually give birth. So we went in the day before and they gave me some drug to start contractions. My first labour had been very quick. Max was born in a couple of hours. Wham bang! and out he was. This one went on for two days. They offered me pain relief. But I didn't take anything.

When it was all over I didn't cry. Because I'd done all my crying before while it took so long. It's not like labour because you know at the end of that you're going to have this beautiful baby. It was something I had to endure. They left us on our own a lot. And when she did come, she was feet first and her head got stuck. I couldn't get the rest of her out. Finally a midwife did come. And she was very kind. She checked out what Edwards' syndrome was. And photocopied some medical textbook with all the symptoms and signs. It was fairly gross. What this child could possibly have suffered. What she would have been like.

She looked perfect. Apart from the fact that she was tiny. But I didn't really examine her that closely. We baptised her and cried over her and looked at her and then they took her away. Then I had to go into the theatre and have a D & C [dilation and curettage, a method of 'cleaning out' the womb] as the afterbirth didn't come away.

We called her Mary. We left a few hours after and went home. It was just empty afterwards. And then, after that I had to find out *why*. Was it likely to happen again? One of the sisters on the ward gave me the number of SATFA [Support Around Termination For Abnormality] as I left.

The trouble with coming home was that nobody knew I had been pregnant. So nobody could really help me. The plan had been that I was going to come home in triumph! Look at me. I'm pregnant. And my baby's due in three months' time. And it was all wrong. Here was an empty stomach and no baby. And Max was going to school in September. So my day should have been full with the new baby and here I was with nothing to do, and nobody to look after.

I'm never sorry about the decision we made. It was a very hard decision. I see people with disabled children . . . and you have *no* support . . . or rather, you're fighting the system the whole time.

They said we should wait. But I didn't want to wait. I wanted my next baby now. I was 42 by now. I think we perhaps took precautions for a couple of months, till we went to the geneticists to find out what the possibility was of it happening again. And there was nothing. We just happened to be unlucky. But I wasn't prepared to accept that as the final stage.

Six months later I was pregnant again. And we were delighted. And I went on holiday and had booked to have a CVS just after we came back. I felt great. And I went for the scan . . . and there was nothing there. I had what they call a blighted ovum. I had what were the remains of what could have been a viable egg. What was the most difficult thing was that my body wasn't able to tell me, to recognise this fact that there was nothing there.

So they did a procedure that they call an RPC – the removal of products of conception. It's under a general anaesthetic and is like a D & C. Then we went away again and carried on. And I suppose two or three months later, within the same year, I was pregnant again. So this was my fourth pregnancy. And this time the foetus lived till about six weeks. And we then had another RPC. I didn't even stay in hospital. I just insisted that I wanted to go home. I had arnica [a homeopathic remedy for shock, cuts and bruises] taped onto the inside of my hand so as soon as I came back into consciousness I could take the pill and go. It was eleven o'clock at night. I needed to be home. There was nothing wrong with me. There was nothing there.

My husband is there for me. But whether he understands quite what's going on I don't know. He knows what I tell him really. He was joking in the hospital. He thought pelvic floor exercises were exercises you did for your pelvis, on the *floor*! So he's not that into 'women's things'. But he's not prescriptive. He doesn't tell me this is what you should do, and that is what you shouldn't do. He's just there for me and being supportive. And suffering himself as well.

Then we went for six months and nothing happened. Then I got pregnant again. And have just had my second baby, a daughter. And it's great. I'm a very energetic person. So I don't find it a problem keeping up with my children. I'm not resentful of the time I have to spend with them. It's much easier because I'm ready for it. I haven't set the world on fire. But I feel I've done the right things at the right time. Although I've always been good with children I wouldn't have been happy having my babies earlier in life.

Yet your life does change so completely. Somebody once said that picking up your handbag and walking out the door at a moment's notice is the measure of the change. That's gone forever. You have to plan things. I did question the fact that when I was pregnant with Clarice I was just at that stage, after Max's babyhood, of his becoming socially acceptable. I had a six-year-old who could sit at the table. You can have a conversation with him. And suddenly I'm going to lumber myself with a newborn baby and never be able to have a conversation for longer than five minutes for the next few years. You can't, with an under-five around. Your mind and your eyes and your brain are somewhere else. It's because other things are more important. You're concentrating on trying to do two things at once. And I think it's easier to accept that limitation when you're older because you know you *can* hold a conversation if you need to. You will be able to do it again, but not yet. Most importantly, you know when you're older that things pass.

Younger people sometimes have no confidence and they think they'll never be able to go out into the workplace again. I'm the opposite. I feel if I can do this, I can do *anything*. If I can cope with this little being and make it happy and do all the right things, I can walk into any situation and say, 'I can handle that.'

People are always horrified when they hear my age. Luckily I don't look it. In fact, I upset the paediatrician in the hospital when he came round to discharge us. I said to the baby, 'Oh here you are, Clarice. You smile at this nice young man. Mind you, perhaps *you'd* call him an old man, but I can call him a young man!' And he went bright red and said, 'Oh, I don't think you can!' And started frantically searching through my notes looking for my age. He was probably in his thirties. I don't suppose he's had very many mothers calling him 'this young boy here'.

The problem with this fertility thing is that it does *not* last forever. You might have problems at 28. But you'd never know that if you don't start trying till you're 38. And the guilt thing that's laid on you. After six months and nothing happening for us, Mike said we should go and see someone. And I'm getting really upset about it. 'They're just going to tell me I'm too old,' I said. And I'd get really emotional.

Finally we went to a fertility expert who took a blood test and they said my follicle-stimulating hormone was high. And I was probably premenopausal. It might come down. It might not. We'll monitor you for three months. The man is dealing in *dreams*! They have to be fairly harsh because babies are miracles really. Anyone who goes down that IVF route. It's a very hard road. So the doctors have to be fairly unencouraging. Particularly at the beginning. But I thought, 'Hang on! I'm not premenopausal.' This was just last year. I was coming up to my forty-fourth birthday. I'm just a youngster here. They continued to test me for three months to see what happens with the FSH. But I got lucky. As I went in I said, 'Well actually, I think I may already be pregnant.' He said, 'Oh! Well, we'll do a test.' And I was, and that was Clarice. 'Goodbye,' he said. 'I need never see you again.' He was really pleased for me.

I'm not going to go back to work. I worked for one of the top dentists in London. I was his second pair of hands and you just can't do that half- or part-time. Giving that up was very hard. To be then stuck at home more or less in the sticks, with babies and other mothers was a big culture change. But I'm glad I did it. It was a gamble. And Mike just loves being a father. I thought, I need to do this. I don't know why. I've tried to analyse it. It's such an egocentric thing to do. *Why* do you want a child? You think *you're* so wonderful! To reproduce yourself? To overpopulate this world?

But before I had children, I didn't know what I was missing. If we hadn't got pregnant very easily with Max I don't think I would have had a child.

I do believe in a God. When I had the termination the war had just broken out in Bosnia and Yugoslavia and there were people having their legs blown off and murdered and all sorts. Some women lost whole families. And I remember thinking that this is just a drop in the ocean, in comparison to the suffering that goes on everywhere. There's a reason for it. Perhaps it gives you strength. I don't know that I needed strength, though. I'm one of these people that are lumbered with faith really.

The midwife who just discharged me today is 35, and said, 'I might go for my third. You've given me inspiration.' 'Excuse me,' I said. 'I've got 10 years on you.' She's a *child* at 35. She obviously thought she was too old. But I gave her hope.

Lea Sellers: *Television Editor and Producer, Journalist, Mother*

I was 32 when I had the twins and I thought *that* was pretty old.

It wasn't a second marriage or relationship. Same husband. We've been married 16 years. We didn't have the first two till we'd been married for five years. By then we were good and ready to have children. I went off the Pill and we thought it would happen in due course. But it happened immediately. And *double*. But I had a very bad time at their birth. So I think that rather frightened me off having any more. Probably more subconsciously than consciously.

I nearly died. It was more me than them. It was quite traumatic. I lost 13 pints of blood. They pressed onto my womb. I remember the doctor saying he had backache for days. He literally leaned very heavily against my stomach for over an hour until the bleeding stopped. So I was in a very bad way.

That whole experience did have some bearing on when I had the next one. I think having twins, although I was besotted with them, I wasn't like most mothers, who when their only child is two, start thinking about having another one. It seemed to me a longer gap would be better. And they were so happy. And then I got sucked back into full-time work at *Channel 4 News*. I was travelling a lot. I just couldn't focus on another baby at all. As well as twins, as well as working very hard. Then at 38 . . . We'd both thought about a third baby, me more than Tony I think.

I always felt very strongly there was a brown-eyed personality inside me, bursting to get out. I didn't know whether it was a boy or girl but I knew it had a strong personality, I really did.

I went off the Pill. Nothing happened. But I didn't worry. I had a boy and a girl and knew I was very lucky. And I had a good relationship and all that. So I carried on, and there was a slight twinge of disappointment every month.

When I got to 40 I thought, obviously, I'm not fertile any more. So I stopped thinking about it. And then of course . . . a few days into our summer holiday and *wham*! I woke up one morning, couldn't drink coffee, couldn't drink wine, couldn't face food. I *knew* immediately. It was wonderful.

The pregnancy, as an older mother, was hard. Sick and tired almost all the time. Then towards the end, the hospital called me up and said they'd just got the results of my blood test and I should take iron. I wish they'd told me that sooner, because the last two weeks were brilliant once I started taking iron. I was obviously quite anaemic.

By now, I was working on the BBC's *Question Time* and I was just so tired I could hardly do a thing. It was awful. But I was extremely lucky with that job because I was producer. The editor was a mother of three, in fact all the people on *Question Time* were women, except one, who was a researcher. Anyway, because we were all female, as soon as they found out I was pregnant, I have to say all the office, about seven or eight of them, were terribly kind and supportive. And made me cups of tea and were sweet and lovely and I never had any negativity or difficulty from them.

But when it's 'show time' on a Thursday, and we do the programme, then you just have to cope with the exhaustion. You're on your feet a lot. I would have liked to have made allowances. But women are *unbelievably* conscientious about their work. They always do their absolute best. I just think so many women suffer during pregnancy and no allowances are made.

I wanted to work, because there's nothing worse than sitting at home feeling sick. But in an ideal world they should be allowed to go home two hours earlier... or something. Just to make life more bearable. I found even when I was pregnant with twins people wouldn't stand up on the Tube for me. And I'd be nearly dead. If anyone did stand up, it would always be women.

The problem is, women have to be better than the men in most cases. You can't be vulnerable, or show yourself to be vulnerable. I always felt it's a great weakness to be pregnant. And it's a great weakness to have children in the working world. And I pushed myself in spite of it. It's a handicap because if you work part time you won't get promoted, you won't get good jobs. If you do get the good jobs, then you have to almost completely forget your children.

It makes me feel resentful and frustrated. Because women do have the burden of bringing up the children, organising the nanny. Worrying about their social life, their education, their health. Everything. And worrying about not being there for them. The guilt. Both ways. Not being at work. Not being with your children. And I've found it too much. I've stopped work now. I don't know how long I'll stop. I'm there for my children for once.

The parenting has been mostly me. And I have been the one who has made sacrifices at work, and adjusted my career for the children. And while I've done that willingly, I thought before we had children it would be a more shared thing. I was idealistic . . . grew up in the 1960s and 1970s where everything was equal and wonderful. But second time around, as an older mother, I've got over my need to be Superwoman. Also, because I'm older, I don't have this awful worry that I'm nobody, because I haven't got a job.

Sometimes you'll go to a dinner party, and this often applies at dental dinners as well (my husband is a dentist), and you'll sit next to a man and you'll ask him what he does. But they *never* ask you one thing. They will not even say, do you have children? Never mind do you work, or what do you do. They are totally uninterested. It is actually a self-centredness in men and an assumption that the woman is nothing. It still happens a lot.

Now I do have time to stop and think. And this is the one good thing about being a woman in my opinion, that if you do have babies, you sometimes have the choice. About what you do with your life. Being older I do feel a much stronger resolve now to do what I want to do.

Let's get back to the birth. Given the horror of my

146

first experience I was terrified that I would have twins and go through the whole thing again. So I had an early scan and once I knew it was a single baby I felt better. And I got my sister, who was by now a consultant obstetrician at the John Radcliffe in Oxford, to recommend someone in London. And she put me on to John Smith at St Mary's in Paddington. He was just wonderful to me and spent my whole pregnancy seeing me and just reassuring me.

I was still frightened, but reassured somewhat as well. I did have an amnio which he did with great care. But when it came to it, I was determined to have a normal birth. And to breastfeed. Having had a Caesarean, I felt I hadn't given birth. I felt that for a long time.

I went into labour, which was wonderful, because it meant I could experience it. And then just as I couldn't stand it any more, the anaesthetist walked in. You immediately fall in love with them, don't you.

The labour progressed beautifully. My husband was listening to Brahms. And I was just watching the machines. The heartbeat was strong and healthy the whole time. Then he got stuck and eventually they said, 'I'm sorry, it's going to have to be forceps.' And I immediately thought, 'Oh no. It's the operating theatre. It's all going to go wrong again. I'm going to have a Caesarean.' So I really went into despair. But my husband called my sister and she said, It sounds quite normal. Don't worry.

They did take me into the operating theatre and I was petrified. Everybody was gowned up again. There were millions of people around me. They had every contraption going. They even put one on your finger to measure your oxygen. They gave me a spinal block, so I was dead from the neck down. And then when they're all ready, they were still monitoring contractions. They said, when a contraction comes, push. I said I *can't* push. But I did. And he came out at once. And he was perfect. He was hardly covered in any blood or goo. And he had no forceps mark on him. My husband held him and I think I was a bit spaced out really...

I've felt far more patient as an older mother. Because I only had one this time. My older children were old enough that they didn't need help with dressing or feeding or anything. Plus I had an au pair who stayed with me for the first three months after he was born. So she did everything for me and him. I could lie in bed. She could pick up the older two. She took the baby away from me. She was absolutely fantastic. I wasn't terrified of doing the wrong thing. I wasn't trying to prove anything. I breastfed him. It hurt like hell, but I did it for about three months.

I often say the best advice is to follow your instincts with a baby. Don't be put off if you're an older mother. It's been absolutely wonderful for me. You do find the energy. If the baby cries and needs its nappy changing, you go. And this business of getting up at night sounds worse than it is. It is horrible, but you don't dwell on it while you're doing it and it's only for a year, and then suddenly you stop, or you ignore it.

I love buying clothes for him. Or showing him the ducks in the park. Or taking him for a drink in a café. That's only because I'm not working. I feel deprived if I don't hold him. You've got to make that time. But that is the awful penalty we pay as mothers. That physical need to hold them and cuddle them. If you don't have the time to do it it's awful, it's agonising.

There are millions of us. What are we called? MAMBIES. Middle Aged Mothers With Babies. I think an awful lot of people feel better in their forties than their thirties. I feel better and fitter. I'm playing tennis. I'm swimming. I haven't had time to do all of those things for ages. So having a baby later in life has totally liberated me.

CHAPTER 5

The Dad Dilemma:

Looking for Mr Right

For many women conceiving and caring for a baby when older isn't the issue. The problem is finding a partner to father their child in the first place. As a number of older mothers pointed out to me, by the time they'd got to their late thirties and early forties, life's rich tapestry was all the more complex. The father is clearly the most essential ingredient in this equation, yet for some he can prove the most elusive.

Elinor London: Part-time Personnel Manager, Mother

We got married, a second marriage for each of us, when I was 35. Both of us had been single for a good six years prior to that. So we'd had a period of being on our own for several years.

Initially, after my divorce, being alone hadn't been good for me. Though by the time we met, we were both at the stage where we were enjoying independent lifestyles. But I was single for what are normally one's childbearing years, the early thirties.

And because I wasn't in a relationship I mentally prepared myself for not having children. I thought I wouldn't be able to. I just kept thinking, well, even if I met someone now, you have to have a courtship. You go out for a couple of years. By that time I would have been 37 or 38. And I wasn't particularly interested in meeting anyone. I had a fairly full life as an independent woman. Good career and everything. But I would have liked to have had children.

I thought that if I thought about it too deeply I might be dreadfully disappointed. I just used to enjoy my work and my social life. But once we got together we knew we wanted a family straight away. Unfortunately, before I had my first baby, I had two miscarriages. So that made it even later. The first miscarriage was at 10 weeks and the second was at six weeks. And I've had a third miscarriage since.

We tried not to give up. I felt I was watching the biological clock ticking. Inevitably it's at the back of your mind, because not only have you got the worries about whether you're still as fertile at that age, you've got the worries of the risks of various abnormalities increasing.

We were finally lucky and had Sam a couple of years ago. I was 38 at the time. John was 42. We just always felt it was an experience we would never, ever have. It was just wonderful. Neither of us had anticipated meeting someone we wanted to get married to again. And then when we had, we'd had the two miscarriages. Any worries you might have about being an older mother just pale into insignificance when you do have the baby in your arms.

I didn't have an amniocentesis because I'd had

miscarriages. I didn't want to increase the risk, yet again. And we just decided that we wanted to have this baby whatever. I always felt if he was Down's, I wanted a baby, and if you want the baby, you accept it in whatever shape or form.

The only thing I noticed about being an older mum was that physically I felt more knackered. Mentally, I think I coped as well as any new mother. Apart from that, I could really say that my age never made any difference. And I've made friends with people with babies, and most of them are a lot younger than me. But age never seems to come into it. Because you have the babies in common.

The only difference that I have felt is that quite often they talk about planning their families over a period of 10 years. And I think, how lucky they are to have the freedom to do that.

We felt, having had one, that we'd really like another. So I became pregnant for the fourth time then. It was when Sam was about nine months old, so quite soon. Unfortunately I lost that one as well. That I found the most distressing of all. Partly because it was one where they picked up on a scan that it was dead, rather than me having a miscarriage. And I think that's much more of a shock because you don't get any sort of warning signs. They call it a missed abortion. The baby has died, but failed to abort.

They think it probably died at about nine weeks, but I was still carrying it at 12 weeks. They sent me home for the evening and I went into hospital the next day and had a D & C. I was in a terrible state. What I found strange was that after having two previously, you'd think that somehow you get a bit hardened to it. But you don't. I found that having had one baby already, I knew just how much I wanted this one. This one felt like a real baby. I know it was early, and I'm sure it can't be half as traumatic as losing one in labour, or a stillbirth or whatever. Yet I was grieving for the baby, rather than just having a miscarriage.

The consultant offered me a follow-up appointment about six weeks later. In fact, he'd never know this, but he was the one who encouraged me to go on. I went to see him and said that my main worry now was my age. Having had three miscarriages, the more you have, the more you're likely to have. And he just sort of said, well, when you're wanting a baby, what difference does a few months make? It sounded like such common sense. I said I'd mentally put up an age block of 40. He just said, a few months either way isn't going to make a difference, so carry on . . .

Then, six weeks before my fortieth birthday, I found out I was pregnant again. But I have to say that the first 15 to 20 weeks, I couldn't enjoy at all. I feared something would go wrong. It felt like a very, very long time. For me, every single day I was thinking something awful might happen. Because it had happened before. I couldn't relax about it. And I was getting bigger and bigger and had to buy bigger clothes, because I couldn't get into them all, but didn't want to buy anything, because I didn't think anything was really going to happen.

I had something that's been developed recently called a nuchal scan. They usually do it between 11 and 13 weeks and it's just like a normal scan. On the picture they can measure the gap between the outside of the neck and the bone inside. And if it's inside certain parameters, then they know that your risks of

Down's are acceptable. Outside of those parameters they would then advise for the definitive test. It only offers probabilities. I had a 1 in 299 chance. So that was fine.

Just before I had the nuchal scan I had my routine antenatal scan at 10 weeks and that was positively the worse experience ever, because I went in there thinking again that they might pick up that the baby was dead. And I thought I was going to have to relive it all. The consultant was very good and straightaway he said, 'I've got a heartbeat.' That was really lovely to hear. I can remember not wanting to look at the scan until he said everything was OK.

I began to relax probably at about 20 weeks, and the pregnancy was quite normal till the end. But I didn't enjoy being pregnant as much as the first time because I felt all the aches and pains. You enjoy your baby more second time round, but the pregnancy less. So Emma is now three months old. She's a perfect baby. And the other thing about the second one as well was that I really enjoyed delivering her. I knew this was definitely going to be my last baby, so I thought, I'm not going to have the trauma of last time.

The first time I had to be admitted two weeks early with high blood pressure and pre-eclampsia and eventually I was induced after my due date. There's some debate about whether induction causes more pain in contractions. It took three lots of pessaries to induce the labour. Then I woke up at one o'clock in the morning having contractions every one-and-a-half to two minutes. So I didn't have the build-up stage, and then I just ended up having every single form of pain relief over a period of 12 hours, because

I was really suffering. And ended up having an epidural and wondering why I hadn't had it about eight hours earlier, because it was wonderful. And then I had to have a forceps. Again, if you are induced, it does apparently increase the risk of Caesareans and forceps delivery. Which I didn't know at the time. So I had loads of stitches and just generally a lot of pain associated with the birth. Though I recovered quite quickly and didn't dwell on it. Because you have your baby by then.

So for the second time, I'd read so many accounts of how people had had a really nice labour and enjoyed it that I decided that I wanted that, too. I decided that I would probably have an epidural early on. For the second time, unfortunately, I was very late. Ten days overdue, which was horrendous. All that sitting around. And then my blood pressure suddenly shot up one night. I developed a severe headache and I was in quite a lot of pain. I knew something was wrong.

I was admitted straightaway, and they kept me for three days, trying to bring it down, and by then of course I was almost two weeks over. So eventually they arranged for me to be induced again, at six o'clock in the morning. And I wasn't happy about it. But I just thought, well, the main thing is the safety of the baby. But I beat them to it by five hours. Because at 1.00am I went into labour. The midwives did tell me that quite often people beat the induction by just a few hours.

I was so pleased to know that I wasn't going to be induced that in the initial stages of labour I just felt wonderful. I thought, this is great, I'm actually doing it myself. So I didn't even call in my husband, because I thought I'd give him a good night's sleep. And then I went to the delivery room at about 8.00am and told them straightaway that I thought I would want an epidural. Once I'd had the epidural I was completely relaxed. This time I had a bit of a hiccup at the end, when Emma became distressed, and had to be assisted with ventouse extraction, which was much, much better than forceps.

I could feel everything. So I could feel when to push because by then, the epidural had worn off. It really only lasted a couple of hours. The hospital where I had it done are pioneering midwife-led ventouse deliveries. The midwife who did it was very, very gentle and very professional about it. She tested to see if I could feel anything initially and I could. So she gave me a local anaesthetic. Then she showed me the suction cap. The only way I can describe it, it's like a sink plunger! She just explained what she was going to do. Once it's inserted and they get the vacuum going you have to push at the same time as they're pulling. There was a little bit of discomfort when she inserted it, but after that really nothing untoward. Apart from normal delivery. And it just took me two pushes so the first push got it going and on the second push they got her out. She didn't have to do an episiotomy, which I had to have with forceps. And I just had a very small tear which she stitched up afterwards. Within half an hour I was having a shower and walking around.

Having two, you feel more of a complete family. And knowing it was the last, it was like it had all come together. My husband was just over the moon because he's older than me. He never thought he would have children, though he's always wanted

156

them. And he's the child of an older mother himself. He's got very elderly parents now. His father's 94 and his mother's 88. They had John when he was 49 and she was 43. In those days she just assumed she couldn't have children. She had no idea she was pregnant. She's said she was considered a very old mother. A lot of people told her she would have a wrinkled, wizened old baby. She also felt very embarrassed carrying a baby at that age. It was almost as if you had to hide it rather than be proud of it.

They thought they'd never, ever live to see a grandchild! They live quite a way away, about 120 miles, so we see them only every few weeks. But now they live for those visits really. It must have really brightened up their lives. Now that Sam's older he can talk on the phone to them. It's lovely to see them together. And of course the wonderful thing is that children have no concept of age at all. So Sam just plays with his grandad as if he was just another man. He's got no idea he's so old. I remember the first time Sam was crawling we went down there, and his grandad actually got down on the floor and played with him. He's quite infirm really, but having that child just gave him the incentive.

My mother-in-law said she found it quite hard work being an older mother herself. She was convinced she couldn't breastfeed because she was older. She thought all her milk had dried up by then. She said she had far less energy.

After having Sam I went back to work on a part-time basis when he was seven months. And this time I'm going back at the end of July three days a week. I find three days is absolutely brilliant. What I get is a really good balance between my time at home, which I thoroughly enjoy, and my time at work, which I also enjoy. I think it's very much what the individual wants. I wouldn't enjoy being at home seven days a week. I worked for 20 years. It's a normal part of my life. I've definitely found part time a good option. I was in a position where I could negotiate it. A lot of people can't.

We're not feeling that we're missing out on anything. We've both had good careers. We've both had a reasonable amount of money where you're not constantly worried. We've done the holidays. We've had a wonderful social life, where you could eat out every night if you want to. And because we've done all that, it's not a major issue for us. And we are determined to enjoy the children and the family and everything new at a stage in your life when perhaps a lot of people aren't doing these things. Like going to the Early Learning Centre! And the library! It brings a completely new dimension to your life.

Like most people we wonder what on earth we used to do all weekend. And when you go on holiday what did you do all through your holiday. Those things that you did used to do become insignificant. So you live your life through your children. They take priority.

The other thing it's done for us is open up a whole new circle of friends as well. I met a lot of people locally through antenatal classes and being in hospital for a longer period than normal. That's something you don't always expect to do in later life. You tend to have your circle of friends and you don't always meet new people at that age.

I think parenthood is probably the biggest

equaliser. I don't think it matters if you're 20 or 40. Or if you're rich or poor. If you're a parent, and especially if you're a mother, it just equalises everything. It doesn't matter. If you really want a child, or a baby, then what's important for that baby is how you look after it. And as long as you love it and care for it and nurture it and enjoy it then it doesn't matter about age. Also, within reason, it doesn't matter if you're hard up. Because what's more important is your relationship with your baby, rather than any material belongings.

I'm sure we will enjoy the next 20 years of childrearing. Because that will be our life. By the time they go off to further education we'll be 60-odd, but it's how you feel, rather than what age you are that's important. A lot of people perhaps put off having children in a relationship. But we didn't have that choice. We weren't in a relationship. So we're never going to be thinking, why didn't we do it earlier.

Nicola Mortimer Stokes: Programme Manager, Professional and Management Courses, Mother

I'd forgotten how sweet they are. Just . . . all the joy. The little cuddle in the morning when you pick them up from the cot. I just remembered the hassle. That's been a voyage of discovery, I guess. She's been a very easy baby. She's very flexible. I go cycling when I get home from work most evenings. I stick her on the back of my mountain bike and when she sees me come in she's just running towards it and loves to get on and go off. She likes the same things I like. The countryside and walks. She's happy to go to the pub and even likes drinking beer! She'll sit in the high chair there and eat anything . . .

So much else has happened in my life. That's what has been so difficult to cope with. Having the baby just seemed, in the end, not a big deal. Because so much else was going on. And because I've got two children from before. I'm a very unworried mother, I suppose.

I had been married before and got the two children. And then I got together with Dave in 1984. We were building our life together and building our careers at the time. For a few years. Then we decided that we'd like to have a child. I had a series of miscarriages. Four miscarriages from when I was 38, 39. I went about 14 weeks a couple of times, which was quite hard. It was especially hard for him. He was the one who wanted a baby. I was just complying. I could see he really needed it for his sort of personal growth.

But, when I was 16 weeks with our fifth pregnancy, with Chloe, he was diagnosed as terminally ill. And he died six weeks later. That was just . . . so much to cope with. He died of skin cancer. He'd had a mole two years before and had it removed. And they said it was malignant, but they kept follow-up checks and said things were OK. Then he had a sickness and diarrhoea bug that wouldn't go away.

We were told he was terminally ill. And *then* there was the question as to whether I'd carry on with it. The first thing he said was, 'Well, you'd better get rid of that.' I thought about it for a couple of days. It was too late really. And I just felt it might make a difference to him, somehow. Although it's ridiculous. He didn't need a will to live. He had everything to live for. I just felt, how can you destroy the baby of your lover who's dying. Especially as I'd already felt movement and seen the baby on the scan. He only said it because he was worried about my future.

We didn't really accept his diagnosis. We thought it might be a year or so. In fact we thought that, right up to a couple of days before he died. The doctors were surprised it was so quick. I was thinking he might see the baby. So it was a bit of a helterskelter time. Trying to cope with helping him die. Trying to cope with the nursing of someone who was deteriorating very rapidly. I had to learn very quickly about cancer. All the drugs and all the side effects. To run around trying to sort out the right support systems. We didn't really get those in place until it was too late. The doctors don't know. They're not experts. It takes a while to learn the system and how to manage cancer.

So it was a period when I was learning very rapidly. And making a lot of decisions. We actually got married. We found that we couldn't register the baby in his name unless we got married. And I'd never sorted out my divorce. So I had to do a very rapid divorce. And there was the sorting out of the wills.

Everyone was crying at the wedding. We decided to go to the registry office and just get it done. Because that was quickest. It was just so upsetting. I went to organise it 24 hours after the decree absolute had gone through. But I can't go near the registry office even now. Because going first for the wedding . . . and then a couple of weeks later to register the death . . . and then 20 weeks later to register the birth.

It was just a very dramatic time. I wondered if being pregnant made me cope better. Because you have these calming hormones. I've always been a bit 'drugged' when I'm pregnant, a sort of extreme well-being. Extremely calm and energetic once I get over that first 12 to 13 weeks. And I wondered, because there were times when I was going days without sleep. Sometimes because he couldn't sleep and sometimes because he just needed sips of water every 10 minutes through the night.

I went straight into shock when he was diagnosed as terminal. I lost half a stone. I was four months pregnant. For a week my food seemed to be going straight through me. When I could eat. And I was shaking. I was trying to decide whether to keep the baby. I decided to go ahead with the amnio and then if everything was OK, to go ahead with the pregnancy. But I think it made it very much more difficult for him. It made dying more difficult. As if it isn't difficult enough, at 36, to die. He was five years younger than me. He had everything he wanted in life. He'd just set new goals and had a whole plan for the years ahead.

He was going to look after the baby, you see. He was going to be the main parent. We had a philosophy in our relationship, that relationships were about helping each other to grow, and achieve and do what you want to do in the world. I was wanting to develop my career. We just had it all so sorted. We'd moved in here, and loved our home. When you think how some people aren't happy it seems rather ironic, doesn't it . . . We were very happy.

The last thing he said to me was 'Take care' . . . That was nice. So at this point I was 41, pregnant and a widow. I sorted the funeral out. We all went back to the house. We had a hundred people and that went quite well. I went back to work the week after.

In fact, I ignored the pregnancy, I think. I always take a lot of exercise when I'm stressed. I cycled every day and swam and joined the health club. And I just find exercise and work so helpful. The work means you focus. And in my job you focus on people less able to cope than you are. You can't stand up in front of a group of managers and try to develop systems and things and think of something else. You have to be *there*. And something that's so absorbing and so interactive helps. And my older daughters are wonderful. Extremely supportive.

I just went along to the bare minimum of doctor's appointments that I could get away with. I was quite elusive. I found it very hard to cope. I was very traumatised by my previous two births, which were dreadful. I'd had an emergency Caesarean after 24 hours of labour and the baby nearly died, the first time. The second time, because of having a Caesarean two years before, it was a very deep forceps. Very sort of technical and nasty. So I'd always been very frightened of the birth for this third baby. So I just shelved it. And didn't think about it and wouldn't go to the hospital. I didn't go to any of the classes. The midwife asked me to, but I just said no.

I found scans very difficult. Because David had a scan. And it meant going to the same place. I just couldn't cope with hospitals.

When it came time I drove myself into the hospital to have the baby. I had to be induced. But before that I ended up in hospital on Christmas Day because some test had shown up some sort of infection when my temperature went up and down very quickly. I discharged myself after about two hours. That's an indication of what older women can be like. They must have thought, 'This is a stroppy lady.'

I think what it is, you don't sit there and simmer. You think, 'What are my options' and do it. You don't worry what people think of you. It's just confidence. And you recognise your own rights. You're in charge of your own body. I get annoyed when people talk about being 'released' from hospital. It's just so negative. You find you're not in control.

I think it might have done some good. Because when I finally did go in to have the baby a couple of days later they knew I wasn't going to take any nonsense. Though I do think they treat you differently now. They've improved no end since I had my first babies.

I hadn't really come to terms with having the baby without Dave being there. And I'd shelved my concerns about the actual fear. But the birth was very straightforward. It was almost all over within an hour. I had been determined to have every pain relief going. But the speed meant I had none because there wasn't time to have anything except gas and air. I'd wanted an epidural, but the anaesthetist arrived as I was giving birth. So that was too late and I was a bit cross. He arrived just in time to say, 'Push'.

My daughter was my birth partner and she was just brilliant. She must have been 16. Just so supportive. Rubbing this and rubbing that. And holding my hand. Not telling anyone how I swore! It was nice when it was over, but it was too fast. Though it was great it all went so well.

I mean I was on my bike in three days. I felt so well, compared to what I was like when I had the babies before. I had the baby in the evening and I was out of the hospital by ten o'clock the next morning.

Once she was born . . . you're high anyway. You've done it. I was worried about Dave not being there in the middle of the night. For the feeds and doing them on my own. All those moments you share. But in the event I was more worried about them beforehand than when they were there. So I think from the moment I had her there was this sort of joy for the baby.

One thing I learnt as Dave was dying, which has stayed with me, was actually to extract moments of pleasure where you can. That was something we were trying to do. So that we weren't in total misery and depression constantly. Just to focus. You know, you get in the shower and the shower feels nice. And you have a nice moment every day, every time. I think that's something I can do now, that I've got with me for life.

I pick up the baby and I just feel pleasure. And I think maybe that's something I've learnt. I go out in the country and I seem to have a sharper enjoyment of the birds singing because we tried so hard to find joyful moments. For those six weeks. It's almost a habit now. You sort of put aside misery, depression, anxiety.

I don't really feel I'm bringing her up on my own because I've got two other children. Sometimes I do. Lisa's doing A levels at the moment. So she's terribly focused and organised, with superb time management skills. So that means that I say, 'Oh, can you look after the baby for 45 minutes.' And she says, 'Ohhhhhh, I can't. I'm planning to do this, this and this for the next three-quarters of an hour.' But on the whole they are very involved.

I've got a very good nanny. She loves my baby. She's just had a baby herself and the two babies get on beautifully. I think as far as nannies are concerned I've always gone on personal recommendations. So I asked around. And everyone told me that she never talked crossly to the children she was looking after. I was impressed when I went to meet her for the first time. She was there with another nanny and even more children. They both put the children first. And that was obviously a habit. It wasn't just put on because I was there.

I felt entirely confident leaving the baby with her. I think a lot more mothers are a lot more protective of their children than I am. I give my children a lot of freedom. Certainly my older ones. It's probably healthy neglect.

I don't miss my baby during the day. I love her. But I do get a lot of her. She was 14 weeks when I went back. I breastfed her after I'd gone back, a couple of feeds before I went to work, and when I came back at night. Sometimes when she woke up at night, which she hardly ever did, I'd think oh, goody goody, I can have a cuddle. Sometimes I don't see her for 24 hours. Because she's in bed when I get home. But then I do have 14 weeks holiday a year.

I really needed to go back to work then. I needed to get on with my life. To have normality. I think because of losing Dave, I needed to see other people. I did have this fear about whether I could cope. I didn't know anyone else who was coping with two jobs, two families, a four-acre garden, a big house, a cleaner, a gardener.

I think your experiences are a gift. When you're

older you've had more of them. If you're lucky enough to learn from those experiences it helps, in motherhood as everything else. You've just got more perspective. There's a philosopher who says you truly live, if you live with death on your left shoulder. Everyone's got losses and experiences as they get older.

An older mother surely doesn't worry about the things you worry about when you're a younger mother. Like whether people think it's important the baby's got ironed clothes.

My baby is delightful. She's just this easygoing, happy, loving little girl. Quite bright. Comes up and gives you kisses. But most of all just seems very laid-back. Loves eating. Loves being social. Loves being outdoors. And this laid-back, easygoing trait is like some parts of him.

I'm coming to terms with the fact that I'll be 65 by the time I've finished paying for her degree. But my older daughters have been reassuring. Because a lot of their friends have got older mothers now.

If anyone is thinking of being an older mother I'd just say, go ahead. You can cope with motherhood so much better when older. You have so much more perspective on life. And now there are so many other older mothers around there shouldn't be the stigma for the child. It's another learning experience, and a very joyful one.

Ellie Thomas: Shiatsu Practitioner

I had been wanting to have a child for about four years before I actually conceived. I just wasn't with the right person. I was going through a series of very messy relationships. They were with men who weren't ready for commitment, and were very frightened about my clarity about wanting to have a child.

And my present partner, Iowan's father, was also terrified at the beginning. And now he is the most ecstatic, doting father you could ever meet. But my general experience of the men that I've been with just makes one feel so wobbly, in a way. Because you just want to have all the support you can get at that stage. And you're feeling like you're going into it on your own.

But once Angus realised that as well, he rallied round a bit more. There was less fear. We'd been together for two-and-a-half years, but I'd only been living with him for 10 months. It was a battle at the beginning to persuade him to try for a baby. I thought I'd have to give up with Angus and the relationship at that point. You just feel like throwing that packet of condoms across the room.

This was probably the third relationship that I'd been in that I wanted to make a go of. I think he just gradually started to soften about it. I don't think that he really believed that we could conceive a child, actually. We thought we'd be at it for months. And it happened virtually the first time we stopped using contraception! It was a bit of a mind-blower.

The pregnancy, physically, was absolutely fine. I sailed through it. I was pretty fit when I got pregnant. I would say that for me, the emotional aspects of it all were far more traumatic than the physical. My emotions are very much on the surface. And I went through a lot of stuff about my feelings about mothering and my own mother. Even in my pregnancy. Lots and lots of tears in the first 12 to 15 weeks. They were about letting go the other part of me, of my past. I knew that it was a moving on to a completely different phase of my life. And I was letting go of a sort of carefreeness and a childishness. I knew I was taking on this huge responsibility and that it was incredibly exciting. But it was also quite scary. My relationship with my mother had always been very, very close. There was a big gap between me and my sisters. So my mother and I were at home together and very intimate.

I got much stronger and more into my stride with the pregnancy by about the middle section, which was just very happy. I felt very well. I forgot I was pregnant. I wasn't concentrating so much on what it was all about. It's such a weird period of time, those nine months. It's like travelling at the speed of a camel. Because in a way it feels like forever, but on the other hand it goes really quickly. It feels completely the right time as a rite of passage because you feel like you couldn't go on much longer. But I wasn't one of these women who was dying for it to come. When it got to the end I was thinking, oh dear, I don't think I'm quite ready for this.

I think I was quite frightened of the birth. I think I buried quite a lot of that. It was deep-down, submerged panic. I think I felt numb and I was going to all these birth classes and talking about epidurals and contractions. I'd read myself into a cocked hat about the whole thing. I think I over-read. That was a bit of a downfall really.

I was doing all the reading for my partner as well. Because he didn't read anything. I minded about that. He does a lot of reading in his work as a solicitor and he just doesn't have time to do it at home. And I would throw chapters of books at him and say, 'Please read this, because it's really important.'

I had a very long and difficult labour, because the baby was posterior lie. I still, to this day, don't know whether it was normal childbirth pain and I've just got a very low pain threshold or what. Basically I just stayed at 3 centimetres for 12 hours, labouring on with this terrible, terrible lower back pain. And I'd been very anti-intervention. And I went to a hospital which had a birthing pool. But eventually I had to have an epidural because I was just whacked. I couldn't go on. I just didn't have an ounce of energy left. I'd always said the last thing I'll do is have an epidural. And it saved me completely. It worked really well for me because by the time it wore off, the baby was coming and so I got through all the nasty bits and I was able to get the baby out by myself.

Angus was with me all the way through. And he was amazing. What he was really good at was conveying what I needed to the midwife because he knew what was going on with me exactly and he knew what my feelings were about the birth and everything. He was very mature about the whole thing. At the last stage, when I thought I was going to die because it was so awful trying to get the baby out, he was brilliant at keeping me grounded and just telling me it was all OK. But he didn't enjoy it at all. I think that's one of the things I feel a bit sad about when I think of the birth. He found it really gruelling. It was so tough. By the time the baby arrived we were both completely exhausted. The whole labour was 38 hours.

Being an older mother is different, I'm sure, in that

your energy levels are lower. And also being around other mothers who are nearly all between 7 and 10 years younger. I find that quite difficult sometimes. Because they're in a different space somehow. It's to do, too, with knowing if you're going to have more, you've got this time clock ticking away, which they haven't to such an extent.

I had quite severe postnatal depression which went on for . . . well, I think it's still going on now! I've had it off and on all the way through since he was born. Initially it was a feeling of panic which lasted for about six weeks, from as soon as I got out of hospital. It was to do with this feeling of being tied to this child. And not knowing what to do about that. And feeling incredibly vulnerable myself. Feeling that I desperately needed to be mothered and looked after and all that was going on with this thing that wanted my attention 24 hours a day. How that manifested was like a panic.

As a result my milk dried up. And I had this difficult time about feeding. Also, my own mother wasn't well enough to look after me. So Angus's mum took over and I went to stay with her for almost five weeks after the baby was born. It felt all wrong. And Angus felt that his mum took over too much, and he was left feeling useless. What that meant was that he kind of withdrew from the situation. Which just made me really panic even more. I just thought, 'Oh, he doesn't want this child. It's all a big mistake.' So it was very difficult. I needed my mum. It was all intensified by total exhaustion. Because I just wasn't getting any sleep.

Being an older mother meant that *my* mother was older. And now, just looking round mums I spend time with, a lot of them have got mums and dads who are in their forties and fifties. And who are really sprightly and can take their kids off for the day. My parents can't do that, they're just too infirm. My mum's 78 and my dad's 76. Another thing about being older is that my powers of recovery are less now than they were 10 years ago.

Once we returned to our own home and started to get into a routine, things got better. Though the postnatal depression continued in a different way. I think the same issues about feeling trapped and tied and not being able to be me, that was the main thing. And it would come in waves. That's to do with an age thing. You do get more into doing your own thing when you're older and it's more difficult to give up *all* that freedom.

I just hadn't realised what it takes. If there's one thing that I feel really strongly about after the birth it is that there is a lot of conspiracy that goes on with mothers. They don't actually tell other women about how different it's going to be. If I have friends now who get pregnant, I do say, look, you do realise how it's going to be, don't you? It's hard because there are so many good things about having a child and you don't want to be negative. When women are pregnant also, they can't take on board that information because they're in this spaced-out state. So I think it's difficult to tell women about it. I think this is how the planet gets peopled. You also think, it'll be different for me. That's them out there, but it'll be different for me, I'm going to be Supermum.

I can remember going to antenatal classes and filling out little charts about how much time I thought I'd have for myself, and how much time would be with the baby. And looking at them later and just laughing at what I imagined it would be like. That I'd be sitting up on the sofa painting my toenails, with the baby sort of perched somewhere. This is not happening. Well it's not my experience, anyway.

It's been fairly flat out ever since it's arrived. And let me be clear, I'm completely 100 per cent glad I've had the child. Absolutely no doubt about it. It sounds really negative, the way I'm talking. It's just that it does never end. And my relationship with Angus probably won't ever get back to exactly where it was. Sex is still very intermittent.

And that's also to do with being an older parent. Because at this age, one is going through this stuff about one's appearance anyway. Am I just going to turn into a frumpy old lump? And having a child doesn't do a huge amount for one's body image, let's face it. Getting back to where one was is quite difficult when older, on top of having a new baby around. It takes more work.

It is though, gradually, getting better, as Iowan gets older and I'm able to communicate with and under-stand him more. And in a way because my focus is a bit less on him now, I can focus on other things around me, like my relationship with Angus, and my work and my career. So I'm looking at the wider realities, which in their way are a bit daunting too. I meditate now, which helps a lot. I try and find little gaps where I can go off and do things for me.

It's very interesting too, this distinction between stay-at-home mums and those who go back to their careers. In some ways I'm envious of those who go back to work. There is a division of labour that I don't have. And I get very resentful towards Angus for coming home after a day's work, and not wanting to talk. I just want to hand over the baby straightaway. And he's not able to take him, because he's tired. There are all those issues going on.

It's been a really positive experience having a child. I've learnt so much about myself. I've learnt where my boundaries are, and where they aren't. It's been very painful. I've been pushed to the limits of myself. And I look at women who haven't had children. And I feel there isn't that depth there. I wouldn't have missed it, even though it's been bloody tough at times. Also, somewhere I feel there's another baby in me. But it feels like a much bigger decision having a second one.

Having a child as an older mother has a more far-reaching effect. You're different from most mums. For many women, motherhood just happens as a matter of course. They get married and have children, without giving it much thought. I feel I've had such a *life* up till now, which has had so many different facets. The intrusion into that life is bigger. The experience itself is bigger.

Linda Lewis: Journalist and Broadcaster, Mother

I'm a (young) mature mother! I had Aubrey two years ago, when I was 38. At the time I didn't feel like an older mother at all. I think largely because I decided to have a private birth, and most of the mothers were in their mid to late thirties and beyond at the place we went.

When I discovered I was pregnant my first reaction was to keep it quiet, so I couldn't ask any other women . . . What did you do? Where did you go? My mother had an early miscarriage with her first pregnancy and I was convinced something was going to go wrong. Also I didn't want anyone to know because of work. People might view me differently and it might harm my career, or at least so I thought.

So I didn't know where to get advice from, until suddenly I remembered an article I'd read five years previously about a private hospital that included a lot of complementary medicine in their care of pregnant women. It was the St John and Elizabeth Hospital in St John's Wood. I went to see them with my husband Peter and we thought it was fantastic. We had a session with one of the consultants who runs the unit and I really liked him.

Peter found him a bit strange because he kept on asking all sorts of questions about his childhood. Like, did you have a happy one? Peter couldn't quite understand the relevance of all this. But I could. I was pleased they were interested in the emotional side, as well as the physical. They didn't just treat you as a body with a baby inside. They actually viewed you as a human being with feelings. It was also regarded as a team effort. The father is involved throughout. Having had the baby, I appreciate more and more that the emotional side is actually much more important than the sheer mechanics of giving birth. Though at the time all you can focus on is just giving birth.

I didn't hesitate for long about not going NHS. Peter was brought up in New York and he's used to American-style health care. I remember the first time I sent him off to try to get registered with a GP in inner London, he came back complaining about the fact that he'd had to sit on brown plastic chairs. And despite having an appointment, he'd had to wait an hour to see the doctor, more to the point. So with both of us leading very busy lives, and me having a very demanding job, I just felt it was the only way I could manage it.

Yes, it costs money, but the thing is, when you are an older mother you're probably earning much more than you would say, in your mid-twenties. So frankly, you can afford it.

They never made an issue about your being older. You never seem to be treated differently because of age. The doctor who helps run this unit, Yehudi Gordon, who's written lots of books on childcare and having babies, is a wonderful man. He never makes you feel that there's anything odd about you. All your worries are made to seem perfectly normal. What you want for the birth is completely your choice, and they'll facilitate whatever you choose. If you want to give birth in the pool that's fine. If you want to give birth crouching on all fours that's fine, or the floor, or a bed . . . whatever.

My giving birth in the end turned out to be long and complicated. Aubrey was 15 days overdue. They were happy to let nature take its course and I felt so confident because of them. Everything was very long and drawn out. I was in pre-labour for about two days beforehand, which basically felt like mild period pains more than anything. I remember going shopping in John Lewis on Oxford Street just to give myself something to do.

The reason it all took so long was because of Aubrey's position – posterior presentation – which means that although he was head first, he was facing the wrong way. Plus I had fibroids, which were discovered during my pregnancy.

We went to the hospital at about 10.00pm. We'd obviously rung them during the preceding two days. When it seemed like it was the right time Peter took me in and the journey from Islington to St John's Wood, which is about two miles, seemed like 50. I was in quite a lot of pain at that stage.

A midwife took me to my room and said did I want to stay in it for a bit, and I said '*No! No!* I want to go to the *delivery* room!' So in we went and I used the pool, which was very effective for pain relief and definitely to be recommended. I hadn't made up my mind whether I would have the baby actually *in* the pool. As it turned out, because of the long labour, by about six o'clock in the morning I finally said, 'Time for an epidural.' They have an anaesthetist on call who can get there in 10 minutes. But that 10 minutes seemed like an eternity. Then I had to be rigged up on the bed.

It just continued for hours and hours. I dozed off, Peter fell asleep on a beanbag on the floor and finally, by about 12.30pm, I was fully dilated. They wanted me to try to push the baby out as the epidural was starting to wear off. I did do a lot of pushing but just couldn't quite push him out all the way. Then they began to get a little concerned for the baby, and said, 'Right, we need to get him out quickly.' So I had to have a forceps delivery and an episiotomy. Having thought right from the beginning that I didn't want all that intervention, that I wanted it 'natural', with my aromatherapy and all the rest of it, I ended up having the works.

I minded slightly. But I was just happy that it was all over. Huge areas of the whole experience are blanked out totally from my brain.

So anyway, he arrived. I was astonished, that something so *big* could emerge. He seemed to be all legs and arms. Eight pounds nine ounces. He was quite red and his head was all sort of pointy. It wasn't quite what I expected! But he changed dramatically in the first few weeks. I didn't realise they all have pointy heads. So anyway, after being cleaned up, we all three stayed together in the delivery room. Big bonding session. Cuddly cosy time together. You didn't feel that you were being in any way rushed to make way for somebody else, and we all fell asleep together.

I started breastfeeding the following day. At first I found it a bit strange. I thought I ought to do it for Aubrey's sake. But I was ambivalent. It's not that I didn't want to, but nor did I feel a passionate desire to. I just felt this is all part of it really. I breastfed him exclusively for about two months, then morning and evening for about eight months.

But I went back to work very quickly. At the time I was presenting *You and Yours* on Radio 4. I had actually auditioned for it some months before, soon after getting pregnant, but hadn't had the results of the amnio, so wasn't going public. I wanted to be sure everything was all right with the baby, and that takes you up to at least four-and-a-half months.

About a month after the audition they rang me up and said they'd like me to do it. It was just two days a week. It wasn't full time. So I said that's fantastic, but there's one thing I should tell you . . . I'm going to have a baby. And I could hear the poor editor's jaw drop the other end. But he was absolutely marvellous. He said it wasn't a problem and I could take as much time off as I wanted. They'd had several female presenters before who'd had babies. He asked how long off I'd want and I said at least a month. And he said, 'Don't you want longer?' Because I think he was used to people taking three or six months.

I said no. Obviously, what I didn't say to him was that I was worried that somebody else would take over the job in my absence. Having just got it, I thought there wouldn't be long enough to establish myself. I told them I'd work up until the week before the birth and then come back six weeks later. I just thought I had to do it. I didn't really think twice about it, actually.

I started the job when I was six-and-a-half months pregnant. I wasn't particularly tired. I was lucky because I was able to drive to and from Broadcasting House. They gave me a parking space so I could get backwards and forwards without having to face the aggravation of the Tube, which I think must make things a lot more difficult. And it wasn't too taxing, two days one week, and three the following.

I felt there was no reason I couldn't carry on doing that, once I had the baby. In retrospect, I totally underestimated the impact of all this on my own health. I don't think I gave myself long enough to recuperate. Though I think if you do go back to work quite quickly it does make going back easier. I have noticed, with friends and colleagues who've been off for six or nine months, that they find it very, very difficult to make the break. It's to do with leaving the baby. Having had that one-to-one relationship for longer, I think they find it very difficult to trust anybody else to look after the baby as well as they could. Which is quite understandable if you've spent those many months with the baby. They become very close.

I had a lot of problems with fibroids and bleeding after the birth. You're supposed to bleed for four to six weeks after, and then stop. Well, I didn't stop. It just went on and on and on. Finally it turned into a period three weeks out of four. I couldn't go anywhere without plentiful supplies of tampons and clean underwear. The whole thing was such an aggravation, having to deal with 'accidents' at work, where obviously I couldn't tell anyone about it. Plus the fact I was still breastfeeding. So my emergency 'kit' had to include breast pads as well. I just didn't really feel like I was a proper working woman. I felt I was leaking here there and everywhere in a place where it wasn't really that appropriate.

The fibroids unfortunately were just too big for a laser operation. That meant I was in for a major operation because three months later I had to have a myomectomy to remove the fibroids surgically. It was far worse than having a baby. You're cut open just like a Caesarean, except in my case it took an hour-and-a-half to remove three fibroids the size of four grapefruits.

It was only when I'd had them done, I suddenly realised I felt much better. While all this was going on I'd also changed my job again. I had been doing *You and Yours* up until about two weeks before Aubrey was born. And then back to it soon after. But just before Aubrey was born, I was asked if I would like to present *PM* on Radio 4. I said I felt bad about it as I'd only just started on *You and Yours*. So I left it for the editors to sort out between them. I did move to *PM* when Aubrey was two-and-a-half months. Suddenly

I increased my work load to four days a week, which was quite a big jump. The most difficult thing about it was that *PM* is a much more newsy programme. I'd been out of the loop of news for a good five to six months at that point. I found it difficult to find the time to read a paper. The magazines that I normally subscribe to and study avidly slowly piled up in the corner of the living room, totally unread. Gradually that changed.

Now, I have to be at work at about 10.15am and leave at 6.00pm. They're the most congenial hours I've ever worked in the BBC. So I reckon I've earned those hours. A number of other women who work on the programme also have children, so they're very sympathetic to the problems that can arise, like a crisis with the nanny, or a sick child. If you have to be on the phone talking to the doctor, or nanny or childminder or whatever it is, you get the feeling that children are not a taboo subject.

We've had the same nanny right from the word go and she's marvellous. She came when the baby was three weeks old. At first I used to worry about her taking him out, and driving to the shops and things. I know it sounds stupid, and obviously he couldn't stay in the house all day long and it's good for him to get out and about and meet other children. Now I have absolutely no concerns at all. I think it's a question of building up trust. You wouldn't be human if you didn't actually have some qualms.

I think being an older mother brings a maturity where hopefully you've sorted your own life out, more or less. You know what your values are, what you appreciate in life. And hopefully you'll have sufficient income to provide a nice environment.

On the debit side, I certainly don't have as much energy as I used to. My husband is seven years younger than me, so he's got bags of energy, it's coming out of his ears. He's the one who chases Aubrey round the house, plays hide and seek and takes him to the park. I'm sad that I don't have the energy that I did, but you can't have everything. I didn't even meet somebody that I would contemplate having children with until I was in my mid-thirties. If I'd met someone when younger, well, I may have had them younger, but the right person didn't come along.

I think for women in journalism it's tough, and I just thank my lucky stars that I'm not working as a reporter any more. In fact it was Peter who encouraged me to move into presenting. I have a lot to be very grateful to him for, besides being a wonderful dad. He said that if you're going to have a family you can't carry on with that sort of job. You've got to move into something different that will be more congenial, with fixed hours. He had the foresight to see what lay ahead.

Yet having that background is enormously useful in my current job. The downside is that if you're going to put in all those years 'on the road', it means you keep putting off the idea of having children; indeed, it often makes it difficult to meet a suitable partner because your whole life is revolving around work. For me, everything 'clicked' in my late thirties, but I'm very aware of the fact that had it happened just three or four years later, I might have been too old to have children.

One disadvantage to being an older mum, in my experience, is that it's more of a psychological adjustment than it would be in, say, your late twenties. When you're used to being single, as I was, then you become part of a couple who'd spent much of their early days together living in different countries and jetting about all over the place, to suddenly find yourself 'confined to barracks' is a bit of a shock to the system. And sometimes I do feel I'm too old to be a mother. When I've had a very hard day at work and it's been a stressful programme, I come back and flop down in the chair and Aubrey wants me to read to him. We cuddle up on the settee, and I get out one of his story books, thinking, 'Oh God. I'm too old for this lark.'

But there are so many compensations. Somehow he gives you a new lease of life. He's got the most wonderful personality, very happy and cheery. He's a performer. He's now talking and picking up words. And he understands everything you say and he has done for quite some time. He's a great little chap, basically. And we wouldn't mind another.

Julia Cuthbertson: Assistant News Editor, Financial Times, Prospective Mother

I had a miscarriage last year, I think at about eight weeks. I had to go and be 'swept out' in hospital. I went through the procedure and carried on at work and mentioned it to the deputy editor and didn't really say anything else. And *then*, about four or five days later, I completely freaked out. Simon was about half an hour late from work and I just had an hysterical, lunatic fit of great violence and tempestuousness. I'm sure he thought he'd married a madwoman. I broke a door. I broke the lock and then ripped it off its hinges, banging a hole in the ceiling in the process.

I think I just had this terrible *crash*. That I hadn't thought about, or made any arrangements for, emotionally. I had just pretended everything was OK. But obviously it wasn't. It was all right after then. Simon and I talked about it afterwards. And he felt I'd been very stiff upper lip about the whole thing, when I probably shouldn't have been.

I had never been in a position to have a child before. I was with the wrong mate, so hadn't thought a lot about it. Then Simon and I got married nearly two years ago, both having been married before, and we felt we'd like to have a go. I decided against a CVS [chorionic villus sampling, an 'invasive' test similar to an amniocentesis] as it was too intrusive at too early a stage. Having had a miscarriage already, I thought I'd take my chances and wait until 18 to 20 weeks when I had an amnio. Which was both the most scary and amusing experience.

Because even then, with the threat of a possible second miscarriage, we couldn't make up our minds. We kept saying to the doctor, 'Do we have to decide *today*?' Because the chances of my having a miscarriage at my age, which is 42 now, and the chances of having a Down's syndrome baby, were almost identical. So it was a real punt, a real crap shoot. But it was getting later and later and the doctor said if there had been a problem we might be too late to terminate.

The bottom line, if there had been a serious chromosomal defect, I would have terminated the pregnancy. That was the brutal truth. I'm not of a religious persuasion. But I couldn't have coped.

I'm very glad we did it. The procedure wasn't painful. I went home, lay down, watched telly in the afternoon. Didn't do anything that afternoon and went to work the next day. And drank a lot of fluids, because you do get these slight contraction things, because they take a bunch of fluid out of you. I never had a moment's misgiving.

Pregnancy is not an ideal physical condition. The benefits, so far as they exist, are that I've had flawless skin, and no periods. The down side has been that I have become increasingly breathless, and now with only a couple of weeks to the birth, even more so. Heartburn, cramps, all the usual stuff. I became anaemic. But the iron supplements I've been on have boosted my energy.

I must say, as someone who's worked all her life, and never really known anything about babies, when previously I'd say to pregnant women in a sort of tone of polite enquiry, 'Oh, and how are you feeling today?' and they would say, 'Gosh, I'm exhausted' I would think to myself, '*Why*?! How *can* you be so exhausted?'

Well, believe me, I know exactly how you can be exhausted at this point. When you've put on two-and-a-half, three stone of weight, it's just an enormous amount of extra weight. And you're not prepared for it at all. That, and the physical changes, which I have found quite bizarre. You go through a wonderful period in the middle months for about three or four weeks when you suddenly have larger bosoms and a flat stomach. Then suddenly your stomach zooms out past your bosom and they look very petite again.

You take on the shape of a little fertility goddess. With these rather large brown nipples, which one never had before. This huge stomach and these little twig-like arms and legs sticking out. So one's whole body image changes completely.

And it *has* mattered to me. I'm tall and skinny and have had a size A cup bra all my life. I don't find pregnancy a sexy look, let's put it like that, and I don't see how anyone else could find it physically appealing in the slightest. Although Simon still seems to think it is, which I've been quite stunned by.

I found I could wear most of my clothes for about five months, with judicious arrangements of shirts outside and jackets and belts. And then I bought three outfits which I knew I could wear for work, until the last moment. Again with lots of scarves. And things which gave a bit of detail where the bulge wasn't. But the bigger you get, the less agile you look. And if you are used to racing around as I am, to suddenly have to walk in a stately, delicate way, preceded by this growing 'wotsit', is quite difficult.

And to maintain a level of authority at the same time is quite problematic. Because you look so vulnerable. But as far as strict clothing goes I think you just have to decide on a plan. I decided I was not going to wear leggings to work. That I was going to maintain my work 'look', which is basically trouser suits, as long as I could. When I'm editing on a Sunday everyone comes in slightly more casual clothing and that's fine. But I think if you're going to meet people like Malcolm Rifkind for lunch, or Jacques Santer for breakfast, you want to be smart. Pregnant or not.

People like that look at you and immediately clock the fact that you are pregnant. But obviously no one responds to it because you are in a group of men talking about European policy or Bosnia. You have to look as professional as you possibly can. And that's what I've tried to do.

And at work generally, you do have to maintain the same type of authority. You have to be just as tough when you need to be as you would normally. I'm feeling pretty much the same as usual. I'm not aware of my hormones, I have to tell you. I can feel that at times of emotional stress I would tend to respond more weepily than I might. But that's been in a domestic capacity, not at work.

The people around me are uniformly male, apart from my secretaries and some of the reporters. But the people that I'm dealing with on a daily basis are men. And they've shown a fairly consistent mixture of solicitude for my welfare, praise for the decisions that I've taken, when they think I've taken the right decisions and the usual level of banter and teasing which goes on around the desk.

Generally I'm quite happy to answer one question, like 'How are you feeling?' But I don't want to have masses of conversations about 'it'. Unless it's with people that I choose to talk to. Because these are people I wouldn't have any conversation with about the rest of my private things at work, unless I choose to bring the subject up. People I'm not intimate with. And particularly... men, I suppose, basically.

It's the way I can keep control. I want to be in the position of volunteering information if I want to. If you're a person who's generally perceived as being in control of their actions and their life and their decision making, and has quite big power of decision making around the place, then I don't want anyone to undermine that or take it away from me, really. It's very easy for men, in the nicest possible way, and in the way of complete concern, to forget the relationship that they've had to learn to have with women over the past 20 years. And to fall back into 'the poor little woman' sort of thing.

I'm the only female assistant editor out of 12 or 13, and here I am pregnant. The level of badinage got to the stage one weekend where I did say, 'OK guys, this is the last pregnancy joke we want to hear.' And the editor, bless his cotton socks, said, 'Yes, that's enough.'

The editor has been great. For instance, it was decent of him to invite me to a breakfast with Europe's top politicians, which he needn't have done. It showed that I was still part of what was going on. And that's been the case all along. I've been consulted about all kinds of matters, as I would normally be. I appreciated being invited and having the opportunity to hear what they had to say. I felt, personally, slightly ill at ease, again because of the physical aspect. It's nothing you can hide at this point! You feel like this sort of vast blob woman.

But I haven't got into that spaced-out state mentally, that women seem to get to in late pregnancy. And I think that may be because I'm so essentially, fundamentally terrified of the whole thing. Being at work, and doing things here, and just carrying on, has taken my mind off the thought of all the things that could go wrong.

It's an 'achievement' thing. That is the worry. It's the thought that you've always had this job, and you've done it quite well and you've been promoted in life, and you seem to have retained this position, and now something is coming along that you have no experience of, no intrinsic knowledge of, and how are you going to be able to cope with it. It seems to be something that doesn't depend on intelligence or application. Because I've met women, who could in no way be regarded as achievers or anything other than fairly ordinary people, who seem to be excellent at doing it, and who take to it like ducks to water. And others who are highly intelligent who are just hopeless.

They have too-rigid expectations. And they're not confident of their own judgements. They don't have the right balance of firmness and softness with the children. Being overanxious. Ascribing problems to the children, which are really their own. Offloading onto the children various eating problems, which they might have. And I regard those things as not particularly natural.

When you get to our age, and you haven't got any experience of children, because most of your girlfriends still don't have any . . . and that's another whole area of having to be very delicate with people. Because you're suddenly in the position of having a baby when they've always thought of you as *not* ever going to have one, and they've thought of you as always there to be their chum, then it's problematic. You don't want to gloat or be too proud or be too happy, because it's not part of their lives. But you still want to be their dear chum.

I don't have unreal expectations of my performance. I'm someone who, when I can do something, I generally can do it fine. If I can't do it, I either give it up very quickly, like maths, or it takes me a long time to get the hang of it.

I went to this class at the hospital and they brought

a woman down who had a little baby, 16 hours old and she said, 'This is my third little boy, and I'm going to talk to you about breastfeeding.' And she whips open her nightdress and whips down this bra, and baby's little face is already puckering up, lips are already going schluck, schluck. Then slap, onto the nipple. Baby's in bliss. Mother's totally fine. So I looked at this woman and I thought . . . hold on a minute . . . you've got to put your hand here, and this bit goes there, and I'm going through all these scientific procedures of where everything is. And her nipples were so *huge*. Her nipples were as big as my entire boob! But it was just all completely normal. I thought, it can't be like that for everybody.

And babycare! I'm very divided about this because I don't know that I want a one-to-one child/nanny situation. I don't think it's very good for the child if anything does happen to the nanny. Or you have problems at some point. So I think I might prefer for it to go somewhere where there were more than one baby and more than one adult. I'm tending in that direction, towards nurseries. I don't know whether I want what might be my only child to become possibly more attached to one other person, than it is to me. Because I'm intending to come back to work six months after the birth.

I don't want a 19th-century relationship with the child. I don't want to be the parent who comes down dressed to go to a ball and saying, 'Hello, darling. How lovely to see you. I'll see you at the weekend.' I don't know. I think the danger is that people *do* have this kind of relationship with their children, and the nanny is the carer and the person who is there for sickness and problems and all the kinds of things that must go on in children's lives. When they're very small. And you, the parent, are this rather remote and grand figure who sails in and out in a blaze of light, and then has to be there constantly over the weekend and do stimulating things.

I'm sure children start to play off parents against nannies, and say to their parents when they're being mean, 'Why aren't you *Philippa*!' So you've got to be very careful. A friend of mine said to me the other day that her little boy, when told that the nanny wasn't going to be there to do something and that his mummy was going to do this particular chore instead, turned to his little chum, and said, 'Don't be silly, mummies don't do that. Only nannies do that.' So children have a very clear idea of the demarcation of labour in their lives. Nannies do all the looking after and the caring, and mummies do the taking out and the bits of what we call quality time.

But about being an older mother: I'm very glad I've done all the things I've done. I'm extremely glad that I did not do this when I was 28 or 30. Not that I had the choice, because I didn't have the right circumstances. If anything does happen, such as that I come to the point where I say I'm going to go off and weave yoghurt now, and grow granola somewhere, at least I'll think, I've had a decent time, and a fun time. So apart from feeling embarrassed for the kid when it's about 12 when one turns up at the school gates and the child goes, 'Oh no! Those aren't my parents, are they . . . !', I feel pretty OK about it.

I've got more capacity for being unselfish now than I've ever had before in my life. I feel I'm ready at this point to give back a lot of the things that I've learnt and to be able to concentrate wholeheartedly on loving another human being. In a way which I don't think I ever was before when I was trying to sort out my own emotions and sort out my own life and being much more hedonistic.

It's very much part of having a good relationship with Simon, but it's also because I think I know myself much more, my limitations and the things which I have to offer. I'm not ashamed of being loving towards something, in a way which I never felt before. As if, before, it was a sign of weakness.

I don't have any thoughts about the child. I'm very superstitious and I've only just vaguely, in the past couple of days, really thought that there *is* going to be something at the end of all this. I've allowed myself to think that we're going to – hopefully – have another little person around the house. It's why I haven't had the pram delivered. I've just got to keep everything fine for the next few weeks and then . . . everything will hopefully pop out, one way or another, better or worse, painfully or not. Then I can start dealing with it.

I had a phone conversation with a friend recently who lectured me about giving up work completely. I thought it was a rather silly thing to say to me. I think people are quite envious, and that on some level, they don't want you to be able to have both a job and have a family. That may be why I've been so understated about the pregnancy. I don't want to make other people uncomfortable. I have learnt not to expect everybody to have the same level of interest in these things.

I wouldn't like to have just friends who'd got kids, or just friends who hadn't. Previously, I tended to not have friends who had children because it's very inconvenient when you're talking to them about work, and they say, 'Hold on a minute, little so and so is just doing so and so.' And you think, 'Oh God! This is *so* tedious.' Now, of course, I think of it in a completely different way. I hope I'm just a bit more attuned to life than I was.

CHAPTER 6

Serendipity Knocks:
The Lucky Accidents

We've heard from women determined to become pregnant who have pursued their goal in the face of all odds. Whether it has been a complicated emotional situation or a physical problem, they have had to overcome the odds to conceive a longed for child. For some though, a late pregnancy comes as a surprise.

Carolla Beresford Cooke: Author, Shiatsu Practitioner, Mother

I was 44 when I conceived him, 45 when I had him. I'd been wrestling with this biological clock for a long time. For me it started at 28 . . . I was always really, really keen to have kids. But at the same time I've always been somebody who had extremely complicated relationships. And I kind of felt that I didn't want to be a single mother. I was always looking for the perfect relationship within which to have a child. Which of course frightened everybody off.

So then I decided by about 40, I think, that it was going to be in the lap of the gods. I thought the best

194

thing I could do was to stop trying *not* to have a child, rather than agonising over decisions. I just stopped using contraception. And nothing happened. And then I got this new partner. By that time I was convinced I was infertile. Three to four years with nothing.

And the first time we made love he said, 'Should I use anything?' And I said, 'Well, actually, I think I'm infertile.' It was a damn silly thing to take for granted. But we both kind of had that attitude towards it. And I conceived extremely quickly. It was wonderful.

In fact, I was in a Catch-22. I had got myself to the point after all those years of waiting, where I wasn't regretting not having a child any more. I was thinking . . . I have slight Buddhist leanings . . . I thought, maybe next lifetime . . . I had begun to come to terms with being childless. I thought, at least now I can study. I can travel. I'm totally free. I can mould my life and I was really quite looking forward to this. It was a stage without pain. Or rather, it was a stage of accepting that there was pain but there were also advantages. There was regret. I would always have regretted not having had a child and I knew that, but at the same time I was really endeavouring to be positive. I needed to change my expectations in such a way that I would not go on feeling like suicide.

I do get very depressed about things. And I was very depressed about not having a child. But I really worked on it. As a shiatsu therapist I treat a lot of women who are in the space of knowing that they will not have children now, and regretting it deeply. That's very sad. They're becoming menopausal, or are having to have their tubes removed suddenly.

Or . . . horrid things. Women who've always wanted to be pregnant and never were. And now they can't.

Once I actually did announce I was pregnant, I was deluged with messages from people who'd always hoped for it for me. Everybody who knew me was so kind and had seemed to always want it for me. My sister said, 'Oh, you'll have to call it Theodore, Gift From God.' So . . . the way I found out I might be pregnant was after I had geared myself up to do the home testing thing. I thought, I've done this before, it'll turn white, I'm sure. But the little stick turned pink. It was rather a surprising moment. I put the stick down very carefully, went into the next room and did something else for half an hour. I didn't even think about it. I couldn't compute it at all. It was too . . . the implications for my life were so unbelievable . . . and so completely against everything I had by then structured for myself. I didn't feel like thinking about it.

The whole story of my child's birth, and his growth up to now has been very much tied up with the history of my relationship with his father. My partner was completely delighted. But he's frightfully unrealistic and impractical. A cautious or realistic man, for instance, would not have been so happy to accept my notion that I thought I might be infertile. After all, I wasn't being definitive about it. But he had been happy to go ahead.

He was in a complicated situation. He claimed to have been in love with me for years and years. But in fact he was married to somebody else. Although that marriage was splitting up and his wife now had a lover and had been encouraging him to have a relationship with me. It was all very odd. And he had a three-year-old daughter that he was very, very, very fond of. So it was already complex. Which perhaps can be part of what being an older mother is all about, because you've had all those added years to accrue all those added complications into your life.

I decided to be very straight about it all. Because at that point he felt a lot more for me than I did for him and also he had this complicated emotional life . . . I said, 'Listen, I'm pregnant.' And he said, 'How wonderful. How wonderful. Blah. Blah. Blah.' And I said, 'Yes, but you'd better come round and talk about it.' So he came round and I was deliberately extremely rough with him.

I said, 'You've got to make some decisions. I don't want to involve you if you don't want to be involved. I've never wanted to be a single mother and go it alone but I will do things my way if you're not going to be involved. Just let me know now.' He said, 'No. No. I'm staking a claim.' Very clearly he said that.

He'd already had a son, from an earlier relationship, who must now be 14, who he hasn't seen since he was a baby. And I knew this was a source of great loss to him. And that having his daughter who he's so passionate about had awakened in him the joys of fatherhood. He was very keen.

'Oh, it's a boy, isn't it?' he said. 'His name's Alexander, isn't it?' And it was as if it was some kind of divine revelation. You know how sometimes one gets into a heightened state at these moments. So I thought, 'Well, gosh! Maybe he *has* had some sort of psychic revelation.' So I kind of went along with it.

He said he'd spend the night writing down a message from Alexander and he was full of wonderful rhapsodic information. Which I kind of took on board. So from there on we decided it was a boy and his name was going to be Alexander. Then we went on our ways and I was trying very hard to make sure that his feet were firmly on the ground about the whole situation. Which meant that I was pretty horrid to him. Deliberately. Tough about all issues. It's a tendency I have with relationships anyway. But it seemed to me very, very important, because I could sense already that he was very up in the clouds. And I wanted him to come down, even if it meant destroying some of his feelings for me. So I very effectively did that. He got the sharp end of my tongue so often that I think he did fall out of love with me during the pregnancy.

So anyway, more of the relationship anon. The next big thing was the amniocentesis. It was great. One of my best friends is a midwife and she was one of the first people I told. And she arranged for me to have an amnio with a very well-known gynaecologist at a fraction of his normal price.

He was incredibly gentle and very, very reassuring and he was watching on the scan as they do. And I was really in a terrible state, worried about losing the child through the amnio, apart from worrying about having this bloody needle stuck through my uterus. Then he said, 'Oh, the baby's touching the needle.' But I, not being able to see the scan, thought, 'Oh Jesus, he's touched the baby with the needle.' In other words, I thought he'd skewered the baby.

I didn't stop to think, being slightly panicked, that they would be reacting rather differently if he had. So I was breathing madly, trying to stay calm. But then I gradually realised that in fact the baby had been aware that there was something coming into its environment and had put its hand out and wiggled the needle!

I was stunned. About the evidence of consciousness in something that's about two inches long and eyes closed, less than 12 weeks . . . but there was no doubt. He came towards the needle and the doctor could feel him wiggling it. My midwife was watching, transfixed.

And so I went away thinking, well there's obviously not a lot wrong with that one. I thought he was going to be OK after that. My only worry was the next couple of days, in case I was going to lose him.

My pregnancy was tiring. I got a ghastly series of colds and infections. And at that point, I thought, 'This is silly. I'm obviously not up to this. There is something not right here.' Because shiatsu is very physical work to do. So I just stopped work. I was lucky enough not to need to work because I had a small inheritance from my dad which has proved incredibly useful, as the baby's father has been intermittently out of work for a long time. He's a management consultant.

So I stopped work at three or four months and I just devoted myself to exercising, meditating, all the nice things you can do for yourself. Going to have hypnotherapy in preparation for the birth. Stopping work definitely helped. It became a very relaxed thing after that. I think if women don't feel too tired then working right up to the last minute is fine. But according to Oriental medicine, you should really look after yourself. And also, according to Oriental medicine, a woman older than 35 shouldn't be having children anyway. Because your 'essence' is very low.

They have this idea that you have this store of 'essence' that you hand on to your child. It's the same stuff you use in your everyday living process. You get rid of an enormous bunch of it when you produce a child. If you don't have very much to start with, the chances are you'll hand on a substandard amount to your child. And I have to say that in my child's case, yes, he is not a particularly strong, robust child. His hair had been very slow to come through. He has the signs of the child of an older mother. You can't often tell until the child is older, maybe in their twenties and thirties, when maybe their hair will go grey earlier. Maybe they'll have poor bone development. Down's syndrome is, of course, a classic example of serious lack of 'essence'. Slow development. Maybe being a bit weak. Delicate constitution. Teeth slow to come through.

It's very hard to say if my pregnancy would have been any different if I'd been younger because I stopped work so early on in it. Just looking at myself as I might look at a patient of mine, my age was a factor. Plus the fact that I was already pretty exhausted from 10 or 15 years of working very, very hard. I think some women manage brilliantly as older mothers. I don't know how they do. They carry on working. They don't report very much discomfort. The occasional bit of lower backache or headache. My experience was of being completely floored.

For the birth, I was convinced I should go into hospital and I was really horrified when my friend, the midwife, turned out to be a politically radical one. I knew she was radical politically as a person. But I didn't realise it extended to her midwifery and I was going to have to have my baby at home if I had it with her. But, I wanted to have it with her, so there was no question.

I then started mentally preparing for a home birth. It did take a bit of time to get my head round that because I had it in my mind that older women have difficult births. She assured me that is not the case.

I thought I'd feel safe in hospital. This is where early conditioning wins out. My father was a doctor. I'd broken my leg rather badly when a child and I had memories of the National Health when it was at its peak of efficiency. I remembered the tremendous feeling of being looked after in hospital. I suppose that was what was with me. So this overrode all my ideas about alternative medicine which I came to later on in life.

But I did come to terms with it and came round to thinking a home birth would be a good thing. And then I went and had hypnotherapy which was quite interesting. The hypnotherapist hadn't worked with a pregnant woman before and she used to give me suggestions for going into labour. But in order to make sure I didn't go into labour right there through the power of her suggestions she would give me a visualisation to do. You know like in those old movies when calendars would flip across the screen denoting the passage of time. We'd do that until we came to my due date, and then we would do the visualisations. Interestingly, something happened. A couple of times the calendar would stop at 13 September. My due date was somewhere in October. At the time, I didn't think much about it, though I'd noticed it enough to comment on it.

And of course, he was born on 13 September. The hypnosis was not in order to have a pain-free birth, but in order to feel in control and happy and calm. One of my cues was to look at my bracelets. That was going to be my trigger every time something happened that might make me feel uptight.

Then I did all the things that you're not meant to do. I moved house. Just the month before my due date. It was so damn stupid. You get completely exhausted. And I think that brought on the birth. Because a week before I moved house, I was cleaning up my old flat for the tenants who were going to move in. I spent a whole day, eight months pregnant, bending over and cleaning and wiping and scrubbing and this, that and the other. I started getting a water leak and that sent me into complete shock because I wasn't ready. I thought I had a whole month to prepare. I was still all in boxes.

My waters continued to leak slowly and because I was with these radical midwives they let it go on for a week. I was beginning to get worried. I knew that they induced you in hospital after 24 hours of your waters breaking. I think it's very unfair, not to let you start your labour properly. But this was a whole week. My midwife said, 'Oh, it's a backleak' or some word like that.

I was excited and very apprehensive. I'm a terrible coward about pain. I give up so easily. It's something I've always known about myself. Always dreaded ever being tortured. I'd give anybody away immediately. And I didn't know what to expect. I knew it was probably going to be pretty bad.

Then I started getting pains and they went on and on and on and on and on. And I kept phoning the midwives and my friend kept coming round examining me. And the pains were getting worse. I couldn't sleep, and the pains would wake me up. And they'd be coming really regularly. And by now I hadn't slept for three nights. And *still* the midwives kept saying, 'You're not in labour. This is not labour.'

Meanwhile, the birth pool had been set up in the front room and the pain was certainly bad enough that I was getting in and out all the time. Even though I knew you shouldn't do that until you were really in bad labour and I knew this wasn't 'bad' labour. Although it felt pretty bad to me. And by now I hadn't slept for four nights. And my pelvic floor was beginning to feel like it had been through a mincer. It was beginning to feel raw. And my waters were still leaking and by now they were beginning to smell a bit.

So I was getting to be in a bit of a panic. There was one of these alternative midwives I was with, as well as my darling friend, and *God* did she annoy me. I'd phone her up and say, 'Look, my pads are beginning to smell, what do I do?' And she said, 'Well, how do you *feel*?' I just felt like swearing at her.

So anyway, then my dear friend finally took things into her own hands. She said, 'You're going into hospital for an epidural and a drip. We're going to induce you.' And I think that was the right thing. It was certainly the right thing to do for me at that stage.

I had been calling the pains contractions and that was what was so awful, so humiliating, because the midwives kind of laughed at me. I'd look in my notes and I'd see they'd written 'contractions', with inverted commas. As if I was being sorry for myself. Which I'm sure I was. Even my friend did this. But have you noticed how many midwives haven't had children... I didn't feel very good about my treatment. I was feeling frightened. It was lovely having my friend there. But I felt very unprepared, in spite of the hypnosis. And very relieved to get into hospital. After all. You see I managed it that I did have a hospital birth. And it was so great to see someone in a green coat! And it was sooooo great to have an epidural, which stopped the pain.

It was still quite a while before the baby was born. I dilated very slowly. But in fact they let the drip wear off. I had a feeling that I did experience labour in the end.

You're so obsessed by this event that's about to take place. There is such a sense of helplessness. You're like a beached whale, and you know you're about to submit. There is nowhere this baby can go, but *out. Now.* You feel like you're at the beginning of this avalanche. There's that sense of inevitability and you just can't get off.

A large part of our brain functions on hormonal input, which is very much disrupted by then. You know, one is legally insane for the six months before and the six months after birth. If you commit a crime during that time you're not considered responsible.

So. They let the epidural wear off. And the pain was unbelievable. Even still, I felt that I'd really blown it and I hadn't had a natural birth in any way. But I do know that I had a lot of pain so I feel in some way like I earned some kind of brownie points. Isn't that a funny kind of attitude?

I have to say that John, Alexander's father . . . I'd been dreading him being there. He is so doolally, and forgetful. He just was fantastic! He was so *there* for me. He was right there, in the most solid, trustworthy, hardworking, loving way that anyone could have been. He hasn't got the greatest memory, but he even remembered to give me some treatment in the critical time after the birth and before they cut the cord. Someone had given me a homeopathic arnica 'two million' pill (arnica is a remedy for pain, bruising and shock), or something incredibly strong. They were adamant about it being given precisely in between the birth and the cutting of the cord. And I'd put it in his pocket two days before and forgotten about it myself. But, blow me down, I had a forceps delivery. All that. And he still remembered. He was amazing.

It transformed my relationship. I fell madly in love with him. You're meant to bond with the baby. I bonded with the father. I'd not loved him up to that point. It was like I gave birth to this enormous love. I couldn't believe it.

Plus. He pushed Alexander out. That was the thing. I was so tired and so out of it by then, that I couldn't push him out, and it was going to be forceps. I had no idea how hard they pull. And at that point the doctor had said, 'Push!' and I was only half there, so I didn't really push. And then I heard John's voice from my left shoulder saying, *'Puuusssssshh!'*, and it felt like a mighty wind blowing past me from him. And I pushed like mad and Alexander shot out.

I was telling people about this moment, a couple of days later, and John said, 'Yeah. I did. I really was so horrified at the pressure he was putting on my child's head with those forceps, that I did will him out.' And I *felt* it. I felt we were acting as one. We gave birth together.

It's such an intense experience. High as kites afterwards, of course. Unfortunately, poor Alexander, having had his waters broken for a week, then had to have intravenous antibiotics. Because they considered him a high risk baby. This is not a pleasant thing for a baby. They have to try and find a vein in this newborn baby's tiny arm. Put the needle in. It was just horrible.

So. I went home. I breastfed. It was incredibly difficult. I wanted to breastfeed. I never thought it would be any trouble. I've got huge knockers. My mother had breastfed. For a start I didn't have very much milk which was also a surprise. And my nipples were sooooo sensitive. And then this other alternative midwife recommended something called nipple shields. And they're fatal. They just cut off stimulation to the breast, which is what you need to help the breast begin to produce more milk. If you use them, your milk practically dries up.

It wasn't a great success. And then *he* gave up the breast. Disdained it and grabbed his bottle with glee.

The first year and a half of Alexander's life were devoted to me struggling to come to terms with the fact that I had fallen madly in love with a man who was no longer in love with me, and who was deeply committed elsewhere. I was in fact a single parent. He and I go in and out of relationship. And he takes Alexander away sometimes. They've bonded quite well now.

I don't have hopes it will change now. This is how it's going to be. I'm a realistic person. I know that we'll always remain connected. Fortunately I'm not still madly in love with him. I had to deal with that. And that was quite difficult. All this, while I had a young baby. I had to tear the roots of my love out of my heart. But I'm extremely strong-willed. Everything's much more manageable now.

The baby was fine. He's a delightful child. I don't think there's been a huge amount of difference being an older mother, as far as bringing up the child goes. We bonded. I think I appreciated him a lot more maybe. The novelty of having this person that I had always wanted to have around. Yet I think maybe for an older mother who's been used to having things her own way and got her life sorted out and pretty structured, I think it's a very rude awakening.

Being on call 24 hours a day. Being unable to say no to this child. Isolation is a big difficulty and that was one of the reasons I felt so bereft at John not spending more time with me. Older friends, who are in their forties, they've either had their children, or they're going to be single and have a life without children for ever. It's boring for them. I can quite understand that. So. Not many visitors after the first flush of congratulations. I felt terribly lonely. It was bleak sometimes. The idea of just another evening in front of the television, breastfeeding. On my own. That was quite hard.

I wanted to get back to work. I'd been writing an advanced shiatsu textbook and I'd interrupted this. So six months after Alexander was born I had to find a nanny and just sit down to work. And that was great. It was lovely to devote myself to something again. And it was *wonderful* to have a nanny that Alexander loved.

Working is good and not good. It's wonderful in that I'm doing what is my career. But it's sad in the way of needing to clock in again to baby time. That whole mother thing demands expansiveness. And deadlines just seem to be a facet of working life and they're inimical to babycare. You need to have space as vast as the ocean, and endless time, in order to enter their world. When he was very little I would have to slow down to an unbelievable extent. We'd spend a weekend together and I'd have expanded and become rested and slow and then it would be time to gear up.

Being a single mother, in practical terms, has always been fine. It's been the emotional side that has been hard to deal with. My sense of helplessness and dependency has been extreme. And the feeling of 'nothing left'.

The advantages for the older mother? The feeling that crosses your mind so often, when you're really tired and your hair's all fallen out, and your waistline has gone forever and you think, Oh God, I'm ready for the scrap heap – well, at least you're at an age where you can say I have had a good innings. That's something. And maybe a sense of experience that you've seen friends go through it. You have a sort of idea of what's what. That you can deal with the ups and downs easier. Perhaps one is in a less reactive state as an older mother.

And I see, looking at the rest of my life with Alexander as all too short. I know it's going to seem like tomorrow that he'll be saying, 'Well, Mum, I think it's time I left home.' I think maybe that's something you gain as an older mother, because you've seen the last 10 years vanish so fast and you just know that the rest of your life is also going to fly past in a second. And it makes you value what you have now. I was putting away some little baby clothes the other day that he's grown out of and playing a Bach violin concerto and it struck me that one has to be philosophical about it.

Jan Hillier: Civil Servant, Mother

Our first date was a barn dance. So we're really committed to barn dances now! It was a friendship for about three months, and then we married within a year. He was 27 and I was 38.

We agreed we wouldn't have any children. There was a 'no child pact', on both sides. I'd brought my children up and I was free and enjoying it. He didn't want the commitment of a child. I think it was injustice really, because I always used to say there was absolutely no need for having an unwanted pregnancy. I suppose you're thinking, why didn't I take precautions?

I'd been on my own for eight years without taking any precautions in the relationships I'd had, and everything had been fine. I'd never got pregnant all that time. So I thought it would be all right. I didn't like taking the Pill. It didn't suit me. The other thing was that my husband's mother told me that the doctor had said to him, when he was very young, that he didn't think he'd father any children because of a childhood illness.

So, it just happened. And having been married in church the year before, abortion wasn't a consideration.

I thought, and this may sound silly, but if I didn't

want to get pregnant, then I *wouldn't* get pregnant. I thought I was in touch with my body. And I was wrong, dreadfully and beautifully wrong. I had just got promotion at work. I'm in the civil service, so I was working full time and having quite a nice salary.

I was surprised when it happened. I was wondering what was wrong with me. Because I was quite ill in the first weeks. I started getting hayfever, which I've not had before. I honestly didn't know what it was. As soon as I went to the doctor, he said I was probably pregnant. I just didn't believe it, really. But having had two pregnancies before, it suddenly all fell into place. I went home and tried my wedding dress on and thought, yes, I *am* pregnant. Why I chose the wedding dress, I don't know . . . !

My doctor quite upset me, and I don't know why I didn't say anything to him. He said, 'If this test proves positive and you want an abortion, don't come to me.' And I thought, well, surely you should have waited till I said if that might be the case before you say such a terrible thing. I think because it was later in life and there was quite a gap between my children, that he was making assumptions that that would be what I wanted. He could probably guess that it hadn't been planned. But there wasn't any reason to assume that it wouldn't be wanted.

At home, I sat down with my husband and we had a hug. We did talk about abortion for a minute. But it was literally a minute. And that was it. We just felt we'd been overtaken by events and that probably we were intended to be parents. I'd always said that if I was ever in a situation where I got pregnant and didn't want the baby then I'd get rid of it. But you very often can't say what you're going to do, until you're in the situation. We had a happy marriage, and on we went.

I'd resolved that I would not have any pain relief. But in the end I did have a half dose of pethidine. But if I'd known she was going to come in the next half hour I wouldn't have had that.

I started off on my own. And thought, great, I'm going to manage this one alone. Because both my others were induced. But nothing happened. And I was tearing up and down the stairs in hospital trying to encourage it. I was there for two days already, as my waters had broken. But they induced, and once they started, it was all over in three hours. It was painful. It's like nothing else.

Where I felt my age was when I was recovering from the birth. I was just exhausted all the time. I was so tired I was lightheaded. I think I was borderline anaemic and wasn't treated. I was very tired for months and months, ever since I've had her, really. In fits and starts.

For me, the difference between being an older mother and a younger mother is that I'm more together about what's important. As a younger parent I was probably hanging around listening to other people's advice as to what to do. You might listen more to your mother when young. But when I was older and having this last child, I felt that I knew clearly what was and wasn't important.

For instance, in the way I disciplined the children. The other two were like a practice for this one. The way I discipline Emily is different. I can see the results. I'm not a disciplinarian, but I know what's important now. When I was younger I used to say,

'Oh, you're stupid,' to my son if he was naughty. Well, they're not stupid. They *do* stupid things. It's different. But they end up wearing the badge . . . 'My mum says I'm stupid.' These seem like minor changes, but you never know how children receive things, do you.

I try to be more tolerant and understanding. I hope she will get the benefit. I hope I'm making her more confident.

I bought her some pink fluffy mules with high heels, which I would never have bought for my earlier daughter. I would have said they're no good for her feet and that they're entirely unsuitable. But I let Emily have them because it's irrelevant. They're going to do no harm whatsoever and the amount of pleasure she gets out of them is great. This time, I'm not frightened of allowing more fun into my child's life.

I'm a perfectionist. I can have this beautiful job laid out in front of me and I'll instantly notice what's wrong. Something wonderful can have been created, but I'll have noticed what's wrong. I try now and look at the wonderful thing and not the small imperfection.

That's important for young people when they're developing, they need so much praise. I would get frustrated when I took the others, say, to their swimming class. I could see that they weren't doing particularly well, but the teacher would say, 'Oh, you've done a wonderful job. Brilliant.' And I'd think, she's not making them see what they've done wrong. Now I know that it's important that they get that encouragement because it makes them try harder and do better. I can see Emily blossoming. I see her improving in leaps and bounds, because she's getting the praise.

My husband has had a vasectomy since, and there's not going to be any more, but he loves her to bits. And he's far softer with her than I am.

The strange thing is, we try to think about how our life would have been without her. And we can't imagine really. But I can remember how I filled my time, because I've got quite a few things that I like to do. And those things have become even more important to me now. I've just come back from a weekend away with a couple of girlfriends. We went walking and Emily was left with family. It's a hell of a job to arrange to get away, but it's more important to do it. And I won't relinquish my keep-fit times, which are in the early evening. Which is a crucial time, traditionally, for Mum to be home, but I just ignore that and go. I don't think Emily minds. It's not the quantity of time, it's the quality.

The other thing is, I felt such a fool in the wider community. I thought, here I was a responsible adult, supposed to be in control of my life, and I'd allowed this to happen to me. Really, it was because my words were revisiting me. But I'm over that now.

Though I can still feel at times, 'Oh my God. What have I done?' I can still regret not taking any precautions. I mean, everybody might think it is unfaithful to my daughter. But I love her to bits. And I will bring her up to the best of my ability.

Jane Porter: Therapist, Mother

My first daughter is mentally retarded. My older children were about 7 and 5 when I separated from my first husband. Then Tony and I got together really quickly. But I just couldn't face getting pregnant again for ages and ages. It was the fear of having another child who was mentally handicapped.

Having the last baby, it's really like having two separate families. The two older children left home in the same year that Molly was born! That was weird.

Hard though it is, it has also been incredibly instructive having Anne, my handicapped daughter. It was right for me, and I wouldn't have changed it. I learnt how to be real in relationships, how to say how I feel directly and how to have trust that the relationship will survive. It's been an essential part of my growing process, making me what I am now.

She was brain damaged at some point. We don't know why. I've never been able to get to the bottom of it. But also my sister had a handicapped child. So it was pretty difficult for quite a few years.

Then I spent years retraining myself. I'd started out on a farm in Scotland. Then felt I wanted more contact with people, so trained as a homeopathist. That took a number of years. But it wasn't the right thing in the long run so I retrained again to become the therapist I am now. And that all took time.

I was in the second year of the therapy training when I suddenly became pregnant. It took me by surprise. It really shook me. I didn't know how it had happened at first. But when I thought through really carefully, I could pick up the odd thoughts along the lines of 'Yes, I would like another child'. I had been using 'natural' birth control, which had worked for four years. But what happened was that during a training week away from home, which was a very deep process where we were looking very closely at ourselves, something had happened to me about my relationship with Tony. We'd been together years, but I suddenly made a much deeper commitment to him.

There was tension because we didn't have our own child. He was ambivalent. He was bringing up my children, but didn't have one of his own. My younger daughter has never got on with Tony. That was long and hard and tough, too. It is something I wouldn't recommend at all. Living with a 'split' family. People do it all the time, but it requires a lot of talking to each other, and communicating.

So, what had happened to me on this course, was that I realised that the limitations that I had felt were part of the make-up of my relationship with Tony, were very much more to do with me than I had previously been prepared to admit to. I realised that I would have these limitations with any partner, whoever I was with. It had to do with intimacy and the limitations that are naturally between two people. It was about somehow realising that I really did love Tony very much. And what happened then was that our relationship changed dramatically.

And when I came back from this workshop I somehow surrendered to him. And in that surrender I got pregnant. It wasn't something that I knew consciously. When I got back I knew I'd just ovulated, but I thought it was over. I was just very casual about it. I couldn't make that decision consciously because of the difficulties around having had my first daughter.

Then we went through the shock of me being pregnant. The question of whether we should have an abortion came up. For about two weeks I was running round thinking, 'Oh my God! What have I done! Is this a mad woman who's got pregnant? Or a wise woman?' But within two hours of having the result of the pregnancy test I knew that I loved the child. Then of course the question of the antenatal tests came up. My consultant said, 'You're 38 years old, your blood test is bound to show up a need for further testing. I would recommend an amnio-centesis.'

I thought to myself, well if I have one and it comes back positive, that means an abortion to terminate the pregnancy. And to me, that wasn't possible. I loved the child. I loved my partner. At the same time, and conflictingly, it wouldn't be possible for me to be around if I had another handicapped child. My trust in life would be seriously tested. It is really, really tough. It is like having somebody around all the time who you love, but you have to watch them not being able to do things. Not flowing and moving up and out into the adult world. Everything takes ages. Anne was three before she walked. You go through a lot. There's a lot of guilt. Is it my fault? Was it the hospital? And at each stage of the journey there is that pain because there is the reminder of what they are *not* doing.

Any degree of brain damage goes such a long way. Now, when she's 22, it's hard for her to separate from me. She's very attached to me. Maybe 50 times a day she tells me that she loves me. She wants a cuddle. And she's got no autonomy. Yet at the same time she's a young adult. She's growing, developing. She's got all the hormones.

Yet even with all of this, I knew it wasn't an option for me to have an abortion, even *if* the child was handicapped. This is a love child, born of a very loving relationship. We've been through a lot. We'd been together 10 years.

I said I'd have the blood test, which is noninvasive. I was lucky. My tests came back very, very low. Over 1 in 1000. But at the same time my sister had a genetic problem with a child of hers and they wanted to do tests across the family to see who else might be carrying it. So I was about 15 weeks pregnant and going up to Great Ormond Street, with my sister, my mother and the two girls for these tests. And the doctor said if anything showed up for me being a carrier then the baby I was bearing would be affected. There was a 1 in 4 chance, really high.

I had a very, very intense two weeks. But something happened within me, during that period. I just went right into all the fear that came up. Then something happened, I can't tell you what. It was very deep. I suddenly knew intuitively that the baby was fine. About two days later the Great Ormond Street doctor phoned me and I was totally calm and matter-of-fact. I knew within myself there was no problem. And after that I had a fantastic, lovely pregnancy.

I adored her. I loved having her growing in me. We played with her. She was very responsive, once I felt her move. For instance, when she stuck her feet out, we'd push against them and she'd take them away, and she'd wait, then push them back out again. And we'd stroke her and massage her. We really had lots of laughs and giggles. I felt completely at ease with it.

We got *married*! I was about four months pregnant. We had a register office wedding, on the Saturday, because we've both been divorced. Then the following day we invited both our families and we had a blessing in the church. We live next door to a beautiful 12th-century church, so we walked from one to the other. It was beautiful.

Then there was the birth. It was brilliant. My first thought was that I needed to be safe. So I immediately thought of going into hospital. But as I started to trust myself and my body more, I read everything I could lay my hands on, I began to question where I would feel safest and most relaxed. And the answer was at home.

We began to think about having a water birth. Which we decided to do. I had a lovely midwife who'd never done one before, but they were prepared to find out about it and help me achieve it. It was the first one they'd done.

I did active yoga for childbirth and learnt about upright positions for birth. So when we got near in time, we picked up the pool and set it up in the front room. I was coming very, very close to my due date and I suddenly had one day with strong and continuous tightenings. Not contractions. But all day, every five minutes and the baby's head went down and engaged. Yet labour didn't start. Eventually during the day I called Tony home because I wasn't sure what was going to happen, and I wanted to get the pool up, because it can take about 4 or 5 hours to fill. So my midwife came up at the end of the day and did an internal examination and said she'd seen people go from where I was to 8 or 9 centimetres dilated in half an hour.

So she said, stay at home, don't go far. We had instructions to make love and go for walks, and just be there waiting for this birth. It was wonderful. We stayed home together. We just had the time together and we used it as a big clearing ground. Every time the fears came up I'd talk to Tony about it, and he'd help me clear the way. The weather was beautiful. It was early spring. The bluebells were out. Everything was *full*, bursting with life. This went on for three full days.

The fourth morning I woke up, and when I'd got up I realised that the waters were going and I was starting to leak a bit. I knew that the baby had to be delivered within 24 hours because of the threat of infection. I decided to get an acupuncturist friend over. I had an acupuncture treatment taking about an hour. There were certain points inside the leg and on the hand, and when she worked with the needles I could feel the reaction in my womb. And within an hour and a half I'd started in labour. About five o'clock the contractions started really slowly and easily and naturally. Which I think is so important, and better than the violence of a chemically induced labour, which I've heard is really hard.

I got into the pool and time went so fast. I would just stay still and someone would hold my head at the side during contractions. Then I'd swim about a bit and move around. Then after about an hour Tony got in with me and he rested against the pool behind me, and held me under the arms, so I was floating in the water, but supported. It was comforting and very, very supportive.

It got quite heavy towards the end. I hadn't had any painkiller at all. I went into the second stage and she was born really very quickly, on the second push. Two pushes and the head was out, and though the cord was round her neck twice they just looped that away in the water. They lifted her up, face up and the baby gasped as she broke the surface. The babies don't and won't breathe under the water. They're still attached by the umbilical cord so they're still getting oxygen.

She was brought up to the surface and the midwife handed her into my arms . . . *ahhhhh*, it was wonderful. Tony was helping me hold her, and leaning around my shoulder trying to see her.

The senior midwife said there was something really special about the whole birth for her and she said, 'If I never deliver another baby, that was *the* birth.' And as a child Molly's been very much *there* from the word go. It's been delightful to have her.

And I'm a different mother as an older woman. I was very young with my first children. I was still a child myself. I was just out of school. And I was deeply into a rebellion at that time. I'd gone flying off to the wilds of Scotland. I hadn't had time to look after myself, to look after my own needs.

As an older mother you know how long life is. If you are having a hard time, you know it will pass. It's not going to last even if it feels like an eternity when it happens. I feel sure we will have a different relationship, Molly and I. It's been hard in ways for me to communicate emotionally with my younger daughter. Even now I find it hard to talk about certain things. Or to ask how she's feeling. I feel it will be much more possible to have a different sort of relationship with Molly.

I often present to people as a clear-thinking, active type of person. And I feel shy talking about the spiritual side of this journey. But for me, risking having this third child was also about a deep inner questioning. It had a great deal to do with trusting both myself and the universe. And I feel the universe has answered me absolutely clearly.

THIRD
TRIMESTER

Giving birth to a healthy baby is the prime concern of every mother-to-be. But for the older mother, health before and during pregnancy – the best safeguard for the child – can involve some complex choices, as well as a measure of hard work. This section covers from diagnostic testing through to preconceptual care.

CHAPTER 7

Testing, Testing:

Diagnosis in the Dock

Probably the greatest reservation about older women having babies is the most obvious and very real fear of bearing a disabled child, as the risk of Down's syndrome increases the older the parents. Yet ironically, for a number of reasons, it is now her younger sisters who are giving birth in higher numbers to handicapped babies. Why is this? Younger pregnant women do not have automatic access to the same prenatal diagnostic tests as older women. So, going by the statistics, we can only assume that older women are terminating their 'unwanted' pregnancies. Ironically, baby for baby, when older women finally do have their children, they now have as many healthy babies, if not more, per thousand live births, than their younger sisters.

In this chapter we will be looking at both the range of abnormalities that can occur, particularly in the babies of older mothers, and the tests that are designed to diagnose them.

A WORD ABOUT WORDS

There is no easy way to describe much of the content of this chapter. This is because it deals with issues that are problematic, whatever the context, and that most of us avoid if we can. The words and phrases used in the following discussion provide an informational framework. They are themselves without value judgement. But they come layered with fear and prejudice. They are the words used to describe unborn babies who are 'less than perfect'.

The dread of having a child who is 'disabled', 'abnormal' or 'afflicted' sends a chill down the spine. Phrases such as 'congenital defect' and 'mental handicap' are uncompromisingly brutal. But the initial reactions to the words themselves are of course as nothing compared to what parents go through when these abstract notions suddenly become reality for them. To be told you are bearing a child with 'problems' is shocking, even unbearable.

It is impossible to soft-soap when writing about this area. Rightly or wrongly, when having to choose between political correctness and medical exactitude I have veered towards clinical precision. The word 'handicap' is increasingly taboo. The phrase 'learning difficulties' has currency at the moment. But are we really to use the phrase 'learning difficulties' when talking about babies in the womb? To talk about a foetus having such difficulties implies a series of judgements about and expectations of that being which are wildly inappropriate. A baby learns to pick up a spoon. A foetus grows.

When words have been used which have an extra emotional charge, no offence is meant. Analysing words and phrases which fall in and out of political correctness is useful if one wants a guided tour of those continuous reassessments that describe the ins and outs of contemporary prejudice. But however much the words change, the conditions do not. To confuse slack definitions with sad reality could be to fall prey to a mystifying obscurity. And unambiguous clarity is needed, particularly when the truth is hard to bear. The world of antenatal testing is literally and metaphorically in the dark. What we are trying to do here is shed some light.

THE GREAT DEBATE: MORALITY AND ANTENATAL TESTING

The link between mother and baby changed forever the day the first investigative antenatal tests were carried out on a baby in the womb. More information is available to the mother now than ever before. For the first time ever, a woman can choose to end a pregnancy if her baby has a handicap which she feels would compromise the child's, her family's or her own life. It has sparked a debate on eugenics with no end. The debate represents a stark choice: either you are against screening or testing, and the possibility of termination, or you are not. The following discussion is designed for people who are considering undergoing the screening or testing process.

First, it is important to note that the range of prenatal 'tests' available are different in scope from each other. There is screening. And there is diagnostic testing.

Screening, made available through a variety of blood tests on offer, will indicate a probability or risk. This means that screening procedures cannot tell you definitively if your baby has a disabling condition, but can give you an idea of how likely it is that your baby has a 'problem'. Depending on that information, you may consider going on to have diagnostic tests.

Diagnostic tests include the two 'invasive' tests – amniocentesis and chorionic villus sampling (CVS). They are called invasive because in both, a needle is inserted into the womb to obtain a sample of fluid or tissue. They both give a definitive answer for a specific handicap.

Ultrasound scanning combines some aspects of both screening and diagnostic testing. If a handicap is structural it can be seen and diagnosed on the screen. Minor abnormalities in some parts of the body can be an indication of more serious problems, usually chromosomal.

The vast majority of babies are born normal. However, 3 to 5 per cent are born with some sort of handicapping condition. These conditions can come out of the blue; family history may provide no clues. The tests to identify disabling conditions represent technology at the very cutting edge of 20th-century medicine. They offer choices which some women are glad to have, although not all by any means. Statistics are hard to come by in this area, but Professor Kypros Nicolaides, Director of the Harris Centre for Foetal Medicine at King's College Hospital in London, told me that out of the pregnant women he saw, who were deemed at risk simply because of their age, only half chose to have invasive diagnostic antenatal tests. Many of these women do go on, of course, to have noninvasive ultrasound screening.

At his hospital, Professor Nicolaides has in the last five years identified 106 women who were carrying babies with Down's syndrome. Ninety-five per cent of them chose to have a termination. But six of the women did not, though they all said to him how glad they were to know about their baby's condition. It gave them time to prepare themselves for the birth of a handicapped child. So not all diagnostic antenatal testing is to put it bluntly, a 'search and destroy' mission, as Professor Nicolaides was at some pains to point out. In 1993, the national figure for termination following diagnosis of Down's was 92 per cent, a fair reflection of the King's College rate.

Nearly three-quarters of a million women in Britain become pregnant every year, to be confronted by a rapidly increasing number of options for antenatal testing. Through these tests we are forced to confront questions we have never faced before, and make far-reaching judgements about the very nature of being.

If the tests deliver good news, that can only be viewed as liberating. For those with genetic disease in the family, testing is a miracle offering deliverance from tyranny. But when the tests do indicate a problem, the woman is in the unenviable position of having to choose between the life or death of her baby. It is a no-win situation. We can only respect the paths that lead to that choice, taken, as they often are, in the light of the effect the birth of such a child would have on other siblings, the parents themselves or their wider families.

The immensity of the difficulties parents face in these circumstances was thrown into high profile when Princess Diana chose to become the godparent of Domenica Lawson, a Down's baby and the daughter of her close friend Rosa Lawson. Mark Lawson, Domenica's father, wrote at length about his experience at her birth. He and Rosa are against testing, and its implications that a child born with a physical or mental handicap is better off dead. To get a clear view of how this issue can separate people, Mark Lawson was asked by a number of friends after the birth whether his wife had undergone the tests. Rosa now thinks it will be difficult to remain friends with such people.

The very act of undergoing antenatal tests throws a question mark into the equation of motherhood. If one

229

does take that first step to 'check up' on the baby, one has to begin to grapple with the possible consequences should those tests indicate there are developmental problems. Again and again you hear of women who do not announce to the world at large that they are pregnant until they've been given the 'all clear'. For the older mother, those first months of pregnancy are often 'provisional', somehow tentative. No matter how longed-for the baby, there is an air of being in limbo. One is uncontrovertibly pregnant. But one may not be having a baby. This bittersweet period can be excruciatingly stressful – and lengthy. If you have an amnio, for instance, it may not be till the end of the fifth month that you get the result. By then the baby is moving inside you.

Working out the odds from available information, rather than tests, can be difficult. It's thought that half of all women worldwide will conceive a foetus with a chromosomal abnormality. But often these pregnancies end in miscarriage, sometimes even before the woman is aware she's pregnant. Of the many hundreds of thousands of babies born in Britain every year, 18,000 to 20,000 have a disability of some kind – that's 1 in every 40 births.

And of course, age is a prime factor in working out those odds. Older women are usually banded together into the 'high risk' category, where foetal abnormalities are concerned. A problem with this is that obstetricians differ in their definition of 'older'. For some it can mean all first-time mothers over 28, or 30. For others, it's any pregnant woman over 35. Some hospitals will make amniocentesis available to women over 35, whereas others confine it to those over 37. A cursory glance at these figures begins to reveal that available finance has as much to do with administering these tests as medical imperative.

Whatever you feel about taking the tests before being pregnant, you may change your mind once you conceive. Being pregnant can sometimes feel like being in a different time/space continuum from the rest of the planet, and value systems shift once across the 'great divide'. You may find that you want all tests available. Or you may suddenly realise that you do not want any, and you will be carrying to term whatever the outcome. Some doctors still advise high risk mothers to have the tests, even if they fall into the second category. If the tests prove positive, the final months of the pregnancy can provide valuable time to come to terms with reality of having an 'imperfect' child, and to make tentative plans.

What is important is to do what feels best for you, and not to be railroaded by either the experts, or social expectations, into doing something you feel uncomfortable about. If you have the information on all the options available, you can make informed choices. Some women may make different choices at different times in their lives.

One woman told me that she had been determined to go ahead with her first pregnancy no matter what, but felt with her later one, when she was much older, that she had to be what she called 'more responsible'. For her, being 'responsible' meant *having* an amnio. She didn't feel, at that time in her life, able to risk taking on a highly dependent baby. It would compromise her own life and her family's, particularly as she now knew, second time around, just how much work babies, even normal babies, were.

Another woman who had had antenatal tests for her first baby felt far more relaxed about her last baby, conceived when she was much older. Having had one healthy baby, she felt more confident about her body, and its ability to bear a healthy child. So she had no tests second time around. For her, she felt entirely responsible *not* having an amnio.

The two women whose stories follow both opted for testing. The outcome of their tests was the same; what differed were their final choices.

Louise Adkins, Mother

I wanted three children. The first one you worry about. The second one you're juggling. The third one you have fun with. But I was aware of the statistics of birth abnormalities and things. I was 37 when Ben was conceived and I figured that the sooner I got pregnant, the better. And although the odds of having a handicapped child were swinging away from my favour, I still felt I was on fairly safe ground.

I had the alpha-fetoprotein test, which I'd had with the other two as well. And I'd always been quite blasé, thinking I'd rather be warned in advance if there was something wrong. I've got friends who've had bad results from this test and they've had to go for further testing, but you don't think it would happen to you. They all had normal babies. But there has recently been a girl in the village who I know just to say hello to in the street. She's the sister of a close friend of mine and she had a Down's result, and went for a termination.

We got our results just before Christmas. We were asked to go in to see the doctor. I thought I'd get a risk factor of about 1 in 100 or 1 in 150. I thought even then those figures were fairly grim. But it turned out from my blood test that the risk of me having a Down's syndrome baby was 1 in 21.

I went completely to pieces at that. It scared me stupid. I just sat and cried. I couldn't ask anything. Paul, my husband, thought we were going to go and hear that our baby had almost certainly got Down's and he thought 1 in 21 was quite *good*.

I read everything that I could, and phoned some friends who'd had tests. So we knew the next stage would be an amnio. I couldn't have spent the other half of the pregnancy not knowing. By now I was around 19 weeks pregnant.

I went the next day armed with questions on a piece of paper. We both felt we were jollied along a bit. We were told, 'Try not to worry about it. We do lots of these and they usually come back OK.' It's patronising. Everyone I know who's had one is worried about their amniocentesis. I think it's a rare woman who can go and put it all behind her and pretend it's not happening and wait for the results without worrying.

I didn't feel good about it. The pregnancy had been really hard. I'd been really ill. And it seemed quite feasible that something could be wrong. Nature's way of telling me that things weren't right. Although I'm very aware that lots of people are very sick all through their pregnancies and have beautiful healthy babies.

I've got good contacts with the National Childbirth Trust and I contacted SAFTA and the Down's Association and got my own help and support. I really feel that rather than be told not to worry they ought to acknowledge that you will worry about it, and give out the phone numbers or the address of SAFTA or the Down's Association if that's what they're testing for.

I've had friends who've been through testing. At the end of the first week I thought I can't manage this, I'll never last a month. But it did get better. We were told if the results were fine we would get a letter. And if there's something to discuss, they'd phone us and ask us to come in.

So in the New Year we got the phone call. I'd been out in the morning and the consultant's secretary phoned me on the Tuesday afternoon. She said my results were through and could I come in and see the consultant on Thursday morning. So I said, 'Your system was explained to me and what you are asking me to do, is wait two nights for results that are probably bad. Something probably *is* wrong with my baby. I know you can't comment because I know you're not allowed to. But please can you find me somebody in the hospital *now*, so I can come down now. I don't want to have to wait two nights.' But the consultant had left the building and he was out the next day so the Thursday was the first time he could see me. So I tried to phone to get somebody else in the hospital to give me the results.

I gave up on that and I phoned my GP's practice and spoke to the receptionist there. I told her the situation. So she spoke to my GP and said she'd see what they could do and would call back. My GP phoned up fairly shortly afterwards to say, 'We're still trying to get the results but haven't got through yet.' But then he came to the house and it turned out he had known my results when he had spoken to me. But decided he couldn't tell me on the phone. And he'd got a couple more patients to see before he came up.

As soon as he stood on the doorstep I knew what it was. You *know*. He said, 'I don't know how I'm going to tell you this, I'm really sorry, but your baby has got Down's.' He was brilliant. I cried and he encouraged me and hugged me. The health visitor later told me that he was going round like a headless chicken back at the practice earlier, saying 'What the hell am I going to tell her?' It's a horrible job. I felt for him, too, as well as for me. There's no easy way.

Obviously I had been hoping for the best. I had a 1 in 21 chance. The national lottery had just started. We were doing two numbers, so our odds of having a Down's baby were sort of about the same as winning a tenner on the lottery. So I'd think, if I *don't* win a tenner on the lottery I *won't* have a Down's baby. You do all kinds of stupid things like quoting odds like that all the time.

And I had a friend who'd had a 1 in 5 risk and got away with it. Her baby was OK. So in comparison to that, 1 in 21 looked quite good.

After we heard for sure, the next few days were a blur, really. We saw the consultant on the Thursday as planned. We were able to use the appointment with the consultant to begin to ask more practical questions. I'd been in touch with the Down's Association by then. So I knew one of the risks was the baby could have serious heart problems. I knew we could have an ultrasound scan that would check his heart. So we arranged to have that. We've a very small local hospital that hasn't got special care beds. And I said I'd like to deliver at a hospital that had the appropriate bed for the baby. I wanted to check out some of the major health problems they can have.

When they're born they may have poor muscle tone so they have problems breathing and also feeding.

We had pretty much decided that we couldn't terminate a Down's pregnancy. The thing that concerned us most was that I might be spending months in hospital having surgery with a very sick baby who might have a poor life expectancy. And I think we put off making a decision. I think we felt that we probably would go ahead. But we said we'd have the heart scan first and see what he's like.

We knew he was a boy by then. When we had the amnio we requested to know what sex he was. We thought if we were going to go through all that then we might as well know. Also it was very important when we knew he'd got Down's that everyone knew *who* he was. Not *what* he was. We named him very early on because we wanted him to be Ben. Not 'the Down's baby'.

I was originally booked for a home delivery and once we knew we'd got a Down's baby on the way the midwife wasn't happy and neither was I, for me to be delivered at home. We needed to be where assistance was available if it was needed. The midwife I wanted, who I was closest to, was the sister of the girl who had had a Down's termination in the village. So I had to check out whether she wanted to be there, because she'd been through so much with her sister. But she was really keen to do it.

To get back to the last few months of the pregnancy. Knowing I was carrying Ben, who was a Down's child, was dreadful. Towards the end I thought it was a mistake to know. In my heart I knew it was right and probably easier to know he was Down's. But it was hard to live with. You grieve.

236

As far as I'd known, 24 weeks was the legal limit for an abortion and I'd sort of decided that after that, that would be it. And although people had made quiet mutterings that maybe if I wanted to do things after that then it could . . . perhaps, be arranged. I was fairly positive that we would go ahead. We'd cope. We'd manage. Down's was no reason to terminate. Once we'd found out that he hadn't got major heart defects, I wanted the 24 weeks to be up so that I couldn't make a choice any more. Once it was up I thought: that's it. It's decided now. Time to get on with it.

But as the months of the pregnancy went on, it all started to get on top of me a bit. I had some really bad days. I was crying when there wasn't anybody around. I needed someone to phone up and say, 'How is it *really*?' Friends were very good. But I didn't want to break down in front of friends.

There was one woman who wasn't in my circle. She phoned and asked how it was and I was able to say, 'Well, actually, it's *hell*.' She encouraged me to phone the Down's Association and things like that. So I phoned them in floods of tears and sobbed down the phone. And they put me in touch with someone who'd been through a similar situation.

And Paul was going through it as well. What happens is that you have to say goodbye to that baby you thought you were having before you could start thinking about what you *are* going to have. We read everything we could get our hands on. We had everything out of our library and they were very good and did a search and found books suitable for our children. Because you're reading you know about all the worst. I expected him to be totally floppy and very unwell. There was a lot of feeling sorry for myself. You know, once you're a parent, you're always a parent. You're always there for your children. But I did feel at some stage they would leave home and have independent lives and do their own thing. You know you're not going to be with them all the time. And I just couldn't see that stage ever coming with Ben. I just thought this is the whole of the rest of my life mapped out.

We met a family with a Down's syndrome daughter. Who was a delightful child. But she was doing well at school because of the enormous input from her family. They worked really hard with her. And my first two boys are just normal, happy, average little boys who have done things quite easily and they get along nicely. But this family did not have that sort of laid-back parenting that I was used to. It just seemed like awfully hard work. And a long slog. And forever.

But Ben was really making his presence felt at this stage. He was a really active baby. He was kicking like mad. It felt like he was saying, Don't forget me. I'm in here and I'm real too. It simply wasn't possible to end the pregnancy. We both knew we'd done the right thing. But it didn't make it easy living with it. And I think as time went on I realised, OK, I'd made a choice, but they were both awful things to choose from. Either you end the pregnancy and you live forever with a birthday that doesn't happen and somebody who isn't there at Christmas and somebody who doesn't start school or playgroup. He would always be missing. Ending the pregnancy would not be the end of it. Or you can make the other choice and have the baby. And you live with that.

And that's not a good choice either.

Towards the end of the pregnancy I saw a couple of women in town on different occasions. Pensioners with their middle-aged Down's syndrome children. I knew that my future would be different from theirs because from what I'd read, children with Down's syndrome 40 and 50 years ago weren't given the opportunities that they are now. They weren't expected to achieve anything. These days they're doing a lot better. But even still, when I saw one woman with her child, I ended up collapsing at a friend's house in floods of tears. I knew in my head that this was not my future, but it was still really scary to see it and emotionally I was saying, This could be me. I didn't want to have this middle-aged child with the appalling haircut, and mouth hanging open and tongue hanging out. The worst case.

Then I went to the clinic for a regular check just a few days before he was born and I was in a real state. It was going to happen soon. And I didn't want it to happen. I knew once he was born and I was back into the land of doing practical things with the baby, the odds were I'd be much better. On the other hand, another couple of years, just to get used to the idea, in some sort of suspended animation, wouldn't have gone amiss.

I got fed up with people saying how they admired our decision. And if anyone can cope, then *you'll* cope. And I thought, I don't *want* to cope with this. It's a choice I've made, but they weren't good options. And people say, 'But they're such happy children.' But, you know. They're not always such happy children. They have the same potential to be as miserable as any other child. And they have language and speech problems.

I felt mad. I thought, Who on earth in their right mind would choose to have a handicapped child? Why on earth did you make that decision? Even though I knew it was the right decision. And I knew if you could turn the clock back I wouldn't do it any other way. But I still felt I was stupid and kept asking myself, Why am I doing this? We've always said we don't feel we're owed a perfect healthy baby. I don't think there are any guarantees. But it's difficult when it actually happens to you.

I was found to be breech, which was really worrying. So it was a scary delivery. I was very involved in it. We didn't know what we were going to get at the end. The thing with the poor muscle tone ... I didn't know whether he was going to breathe unaided, and things like that. But immediately he was born they took him to give him a couple of minutes of oxygen and then he was handed to me pink and lovely. And he was in much better condition than my second baby. Who had arrived at 36 weeks but was very shocked and distressed by the whole thing and very blue and was whisked straight off to special care and an incubator.

I'd written a birth plan. I had this big fear that he would be whisked off because he was 'the Down's baby'. I had written in my birth plan how important it was to me that if at all possible this didn't happen. I wanted him as mine first. I thought it was the only way I'm going to stand any chance with all of this. Is to have him and get used to him and feel him. I thought if he was whisked off I would really struggle. I might not want him back.

He just looked so lovely. He was just a baby. And then I put him to the breast and he fed brilliantly. It was really important to me that he breastfeed. It's gone downhill since then, but at least I knew he was capable. And I'm still breastfeeding. It's taking longer but he's gaining weight.

Down's babies have poor immune systems and breastfeeding can help develop it. It's been a real boost. I mean he had problems gaping, after he'd done it brilliantly to start with. He wouldn't open his mouth properly. But because I know what I am doing we just wait a bit longer. Wait till he is ready.

And at the end of it, we had a baby. If anything, I don't feel sorry for myself any more. Sometimes I feel sorry for him. Because he's such a lovely little boy. Life isn't going to be easy for him.

The health services do all slot in to support you. I had a visit from the Child Development Centre and the physiotherapist and from the Home Education Team. It was reassuring that everything was ready and waiting

We don't know what degree Ben is. You can't tell what potential is there till he starts doing things, or doesn't, as the case may be. But everything so far has been really good. He's been feeding well. And his muscle tone is good. He's not terribly floppy. We just have to wait and see how it goes.

Down's babies now are going to mainstream schools. They're certainly getting to the infants. Most of them are doing junior school. A lot of them are going into the mainstream senior school. That wasn't happening years ago. They weren't even offered the places. The little girl that we met is in year one and she's midway in her class on reading ability. They seem to go so far and then it tails off a bit. I don't really know what our future is. I think now he's here, and dealing with the here and now, what happens in 20, 30, 40 years' time doesn't seem quite so important as it did before.

Our village school is changing. It's going all through infants and juniors rather than just infants and I spoke to the head teacher while I was pregnant. Don't forget, I said to her, while you're doing these wonderful things for the school that you have a special needs child coming to you in four years' time. And she said, 'I wouldn't expect him to go anywhere else.' They're expecting him to be there with his older brothers. And when you see all the people who are helping us get there, there is a future.

You have to do what is right for you and your family. I have a great deal of respect for people that do terminate. It is not the easy option. You have to live with it forever. I chose not to have a termination. But if somebody were to come along and say we're going to change the law and not have termination, I'd be out there with the rest of them campaigning to keep it in place. It wasn't right for me and my family. We couldn't have gone through with it. But I'm glad there is choice.

Liz Sagar, Mother

It's horrible seeing your partner's grief. It was black for him. He shut down on it for the first two months and I thought he didn't feel anything. Then he went out one night and someone fed him really stiff drinks and he started crying and couldn't stop. I knew then he felt just as badly as I felt.

We married late, when I was 36. I knew that if I married Keith I would have children and that was a huge decision for me. But I knew that I wanted to marry Keith. And I thought I wanted children. Yet it remained a big issue. I wasn't absolutely sure. I spent the first six months of marriage enjoying it very much, and also coming to terms with the fact I would be trying to have a child. It took me six months of thinking, and thinking and thinking. And then it clicked and I got pregnant immediately we started trying and had Tom. Which was a huge shock. I was rising 38.

I had an amnio with Tom. Keith was very, very clear that he wanted an amnio. I wasn't. I felt morally it wasn't right and didn't think I could go through with it should there have been a need for a termination. But I also realised that I was probably sticking my head in the sand, and in the end I thought Keith wants this so much, he's so clear about it, I think I may not be facing up to things. I decided to do it, but I didn't do it with a tremendously good grace. And I was terribly worried for three weeks, even though I was absolutely certain Tom was OK. As indeed he was.

When I got pregnant the second time I knew that I had to come to terms with having yet another amnio. And I found that hard. I had just turned 40. I was embarrassed about being pregnant at 40. I'm the sort of person who likes to do things the right way, and I knew that some people would think it was the wrong thing to do, having a baby so late. But I went ahead and got pregnant. I knew I wanted another child and

Keith certainly did. And that was the earliest I felt able to do it after having Tom.

I had found it very difficult becoming 40. I was questioning my life. I wasn't sure what I wanted to do about work. I felt I wanted a break. Anyway, I got pregnant. And it was a horrid pregnancy, I was sick and tired like there was no tomorrow. I was absolutely ill with it. I just kept thinking, it's going to be worth it in the end.

And then I went for the amnio. I actually didn't worry that much about the result. Though at some level I already knew there was something the matter with the baby. I just knew. I felt something wasn't right. But I *didn't* think it was Down's. That was probably too much to anticipate. It took three weeks for the result, during which we had a very nice time on holiday. Then, the consultant phoned up at six o'clock that evening, just two days after Christmas, and she said, 'I'm sorry, the baby's got Down's syndrome.'

It's like the whole world falls apart. I can still remember the exact scene. The Christmas tree was still lit up. It put me off Christmas trees for a very long time.

And I had to phone Keith. He was very cheerful because we'd had a nice holiday. And he said, 'I've just ordered the tumble drier because we're going to need one with the new baby.' And then I had to tell him this. And though he'd been awfully clear that he'd want a termination if the baby was Down's, he came home and I was quite relieved that he felt the same way as me. He said, 'I just don't know what to do. I always thought I'd know. And I don't.' So it took him a week to decide. And I'm a very thorough person and I went into it terribly carefully. The whys and wherefores. Talked to the mother of a Down's syndrome boy, and to different people. Got a lot of help from the hospital chaplain. Because I did think what I thought I was about to do was wrong. He was wonderful.

He said I was seeing things in black and white terms. That life wasn't like that. That all we could do was take the best decision we could at the moment. And that was the most important thing. If later we decided it was the wrong decision, at least we'd know that at the time we'd thought it all through as best we could. That was wonderful advice. It helped immeasurably. In fact, the good thing about the whole experience was how kind and good people were. And what time they gave me.

The mother of the Down's baby didn't believe in abortion. She said she loved her child dearly. She was very, very upset when it first happened. But, yes, she thought he had a lot to offer. I have to stress, that although I had the termination I do not believe people should terminate as a matter of course. Somebody who decides not to terminate, as long as they've thought it through clearly, that's fine. It's a very, very personal decision. You've got to live with it for the rest of your life. Obviously you're going to get some good out of whichever way you go.

People differ tremendously in their characteristics and personality. I feel I couldn't have managed . . . though I don't know, of course I'll never know. I have friends who won't have amnios. I can completely understand that. There should never ever be any pressure on anybody as to which way they decide. I think the few people who know I've had the

245

termination, some of them think, 'Oh well, she doesn't like Down's syndrome babies.' That's absolutely not true. The truth is I thought it was better for him that I didn't have him. Given my personality. Life is hard and I didn't see a plus for him in coming in mentally handicapped. I could be completely wrong on this. I felt it was better that I suffer, than him suffer as well. I was taking the decision for him.

Some people when they've heard I've had a termination say, 'Oh, very sensible.' But I don't say anything to that, because I think I'm asking them to understand or have views that may be more than they can appreciate. I think they're way off. Because they're saying that it's completely wrong to be Down's, aren't they. I haven't yet felt like sitting down and going through it with them. In the future maybe I will be able to.

We didn't come to the decision simultaneously. Keith took about a week and I took about 10 days. It was very hard for him, that last three days after he'd decided, and I still couldn't quite get there. I needed all that time. We were both very deeply shocked. And the shock goes on for a long time afterwards. We talked about it a lot. We spoke to the Down's Syndrome Association. We spoke to SAFTA. I spoke to a couple of mothers, over the phone, of Down's syndrome children. There was incredible generosity.

Once we decided, we went down to the hospital and they started the termination and it was very, very traumatic and distressing. What you're doing, you're finishing a pregnancy off. The enormity of it. It's huge. Plus, you're just sitting there waiting for things to happen. I found out afterwards that I was quite lucky. Mine took 24 hours. It can take much longer.

It's absolutely horrible and is not something to be taken lightly at all. We saw our son. I didn't immediately. I just couldn't do it. I went back in the afternoon. Keith saw him immediately and broke down completely. It's important to see the child. We had a funeral about two weeks later. Just the two of us were there. We called him Michael.

It was a watershed in my life. Life is never the same again. We went through tremendous grief and tremendous anger. I've met other women who don't have the anger that I had. But I had it. That it could happen to you. That you don't have the child. That life has done it to you. It makes you grow up. It gives you a different perspective. It makes you much more sympathetic to other people's grief. People may look quite normal. But they may have something similar going on for them. You start fearing losing the child you have, or your husband, because death has become real. You put things more in proportion, because you realise that things that normally bother you, like moving house, which is stressing me out now, is really something very, very minor.

If something like that happens to you it really matters. I don't regret it. I miss him, and I always will. I'm aware of someone not being there. He was born, and he was born dead. And he's not here. And I carried him for 21 weeks. It's a definite absence. Plus, my eldest is six, and my youngest is 10 months, so there's that gap in the middle.

I'm very, very aware of the termination date.

Forever. We always go up to the grave. It's always remembered and always will be. I will always know that one of my children is dead.

NATURE'S VARIATIONS: THE DISABILITIES DESCRIBED

Before we look at the tests themselves, let's be clear about what they are trying to find out. Though the fear of Down's syndrome is the one handicap that concerns most older women, I am going to describe all the major handicaps. The value of doing so is that although different tests are used to identify different problems, a number of those tests can be used for identifying Down's. It is worth having a broad overview in order to make an informed choice.

Disabilities fall into three distinct categories, as follows.

Physical defects
These defects are also known as congenital malformations. 'Congenital' simply means that the defect is present when the child is born. They form the largest group of handicap. Ultrasound scanning is primarily used to identify this group. Heart defects are the most common congenital malformations. Limb deformities are the next most common, then come problems of the central nervous system. Spina bifida is, for instance, a defect of the central nervous system.

Some physical defects can be inherited from parents. But most are completely unexpected and are called 'sporadic'. Of the babies born with defects in one year, around 1,400 are inherited and between 10,500 to 14,000 are sporadic.

Inherited genetic disease

Inherited genetic diseases are the next most common handicapping condition. Every cell in our body contains a unique blueprint. If the parents pass on a significant alteration to that blueprint, genetic disease can occur. Cystic fibrosis is a common inherited genetic disease.

Chromosome disorders

Down's syndrome comes under this heading. These disorders are generally not inherited, but are caused by a poor separation of chromosomes, initially within the sperm or the egg, or later, at conception. Chromosomal syndromes are in evidence from the very first moment of conception and nothing that was done or not done during pregnancy could have caused or prevented them.

Ninety-five per cent of cases of Down's syndrome are due to chance and result from a chromosomal disorder called a 'trisomy', when there is an extra, unpaired, chromosome. In every normal cell, 46 chromosomes are arranged in 23 matching pairs. But in Down's syndrome there is an extra chromosome in the twenty-first pair. Thus, another name for Down's syndrome is Trisomy 21. It is the most common cause of mental handicap, and involves learning difficulties as well as possible physical problems.

It's thought that nearly half of all babies with Down's syndrome are miscarried early in pregnancy. The overall incidence of having a baby with Down's syndrome is 1 in 650 live births. The chances of it happening while you are still in your twenties are low, but after you reach 35, they start moving up.

Mother's age	Approximate risk of affected child (1 in . . .)
20	2,000
25	1,205
30	900
35	400
36	290
37	225
38	180
39	140
40	109
41	85
42	70
43	50
44	40
45	32
46	25
47	20
48	15
49	12

MOMENTS OF TRUTH: TESTS AND SCREENING

First and most importantly, it is essential to understand what tests cannot do. Antenatal tests are specific. If you go in for screening, that means having a blood test; and the results of that test will give a level of probability or risk. Probability or risk means there is a likelihood of there being a foetal abnormality of some sort.

Diagnostic testing is different. It is more specific. If you are looking for a genetic disease using amniocentesis you are carrying out a diagnostic test for that disorder. If the questions you are asking are about chromosomes, the answer will precisely relate to that. The test will not necessarily reveal physical defects.

If you have an amniocentesis, or an even newer form of diagnostic test called chorionic villus sampling (CVS), specimens of your baby's cells are taken. These reveal the sex of your baby, and whether the chromosomes are the correct shape and size and are present in the correct number.

Amniocentesis and chorionic villus sampling detect both genetic disease and chromosome disorders. What amniocentesis and CVS do not reveal, as diagnostic tests, is whether your baby has a heart defect or other physical problem. A number of procedures may be carried out to test for a number of contingencies. For instance, if the doctor notices on an ultrasound scan that a foetus has a heart defect, it might be useful to then apply CVS, the diagnostic test, because heart defects often combine with chromosomal disorders. Down's syndrome is a chromosomal disorder, and 50 per cent of Down's babies have heart defects too.

Another type of test is cordocentesis, which is yet again a way of analysing the baby's chromosomes by examining its white blood cells.

Over the following pages I discuss all the tests and screening available.

The biochemical screenings
Biochemical screenings are analyses of the mother's blood. You can tell a lot about the health of a baby this way.

What happens is that a very small amount of the baby's blood combines with the mother's through the placenta. The placenta is attached to the uterus by many tiny, frond-like filaments, the villi, which are well supplied with blood from the baby. Though they are covered with extremely

251

thin layers of skin, substances such as oxygen, carbon dioxide and hormones pass across from the baby into the mother. This skin ensures that, on the whole, the blood of mother and baby never actually mix. Sometimes, though, the very fine skin of the villi tears, and a small amount of blood may cross too. When the mother's blood is taken and 'screened', the admixture of foetal blood is analysed, either through the Alpha-fetoprotein test or the triple test.

Alpha-fetoprotein Test. Alpha-fetoprotein (AFP) is a substance synthesised by the baby's liver, and found in large quantities in its skin and muscles. Some AFP normally leaves the baby via its urine, so small quantities can be found in the amniotic fluid as well.

But if the levels of AFP are too high they can indicate a leak from the baby. Neural tube defects (NTDs) are a series of conditions where this is happening. If there is an opening in the skin, as there usually is with NTDs, the protein leaks out of the baby into the amniotic fluid in greater quantities. It passes from there, via the placenta, into the mother's blood. But some NTDs have what are called 'closed lesions', and these defects are harder to detect because there are no signs of raised protein levels in the amniotic fluid.

NTDs occur in about 4 to 5 per 1,000 births. The risk of having a baby with an NTD increases tenfold if you have already had an affected child. But 95 per cent of babies with NTDs are born to people with no family history of them.

Different levels of the protein indicate different things. High levels may indicate a central nervous system disorder such as spina bifida or anencephaly. In spina bifida there is a problem with the central nervous cord, which most often remains open instead of closing over. With anencephaly, the covering of the brain remains incomplete and these babies always die at, or soon after, birth.

Low levels of alpha-fetoprotein suggest that the mother may be at greater risk of carrying a child with Down's syndrome.

The AFP levels vary naturally during pregnancy, the concentration rising gradually to its maximum amount at about the thirtieth week. And this is the problem with AFP screening. If, for instance, it appears that levels are high, it could mean simply that you are later into pregnancy than first calculated. It may be worth having a scan before an AFP test to confirm dates more exactly.

Levels can also be high if you're carrying more than one baby, and particularly identical twins. Boys often cause higher levels than girls. A mother's weight and race also influence the levels of proteins: thin women have consistently tested to have higher levels of AFP than fat women. Levels are often naturally low if you are an insulin-dependent diabetic. It's important to remember that there is no one level which clearly and incontrovertibly indicates abnormality.

Most women who have either 'high' or 'low' levels go on to have perfectly normal babies. But if your level is especially high, or low, you may be called back again after a week. This happens to about 1 in 20 women. Sometimes AFP is done routinely and you may not even know it's being carried out, as it can be combined with other blood tests. Check local policy if that's something you don't want to happen.

The test is usually carried out some time around the sixteenth to eighteenth week of pregnancy. And it is generally about 90 per cent accurate in diagnosing abnormality. It is only a screening, which will tell you whether you have an increased risk of having a baby with either an NTD or Down's. If an increased risk is indicated, then you may choose to have a diagnostic test, which will give more specific information.

It is rare for a mother to be told there is a problem when there is not, but it can happen. That is called a 'false positive'. Perhaps worse than that is the 'false negative', when a mother is told there is no problem when there is. These occur too, though less often.

Not all health authorities provide AFP. It may be that they feel that the incidence of NTDs is very low in their area and they would rather put resources into something else. Some health authorities do the triple test, which includes an AFP test and a number of others which I describe later.

The incidence of babies with NTDs has fallen by 75 per cent among women who have been screened. However, that isn't entirely due to screening *per se*. It seems that the natural incidence of these handicaps are declining.

Your results should take about a week to come through. Procedures vary from region to region. Some health authorities tell the mother that she has been given the all-clear, while others do not get in touch unless there's a problem. If you feel you would like to know when the results are through, and what those results are, regardless, it might be worth specifying that.

With all the uncertainties of the test, you may wonder, 'Why bother in the first place?' The reason is that AFP can act as a signpost, suggesting possibilities. High AFP levels can indicate it is worth investigating further. And a high AFP may be useful in other ways. For instance, sometimes it can mean there are problems with the placenta. In such a case, the doctor can be alerted to the fact, and therefore more carefully monitor the pregnancy as it progresses.

The disadvantage of the test is that if you do have a positive result, you may have a three-week gap before you have a further AFP test, a scan or an amnio. And your baby may be normal all along. That can be a stressful time. It is worth being very clear over why you want the test, and what you intend to do with the results, whatever they may be, because you may end up wishing you have started on another route. You may opt, for instance, for the triple test, which will screen for more things, including the possibility of Down's syndrome.

The Triple Test. The triple test – also known as maternal serum testing or the Bart's test, as it was first developed at St Bartholomew's Hospital in London – is really the same thing as an AFP screening, with two more procedures added. The levels of protein are measured in the mother's blood, along with an analysis of two more chemicals: unconjugate oestriol and human chorionic gonadotrophin (HCG), a hormone.

In the description of AFP testing, I mentioned that a low level of AFP can be an indication of a greater risk of Down's. It is not, in itself, a sufficiently accurate screening test. But if, in conjunction with a low level of AFP, low levels of the mother's blood oestriol and high levels of HCG are also found, what begins to emerge is a more compelling indication of possible disability. And if those three findings are then combined with the mother's age and length of gestation, a more predictive picture builds up. Using these indicators, up to 60 per cent of Down's babies are detected.

So, the triple test is one way of pulling together not just factors such as your age, but others which are just as unique to you. Risks can dramatically reduce. A 40-year-old woman could start with a potential risk of 1 in 126 of having a Down's baby on her delivery day. But once she has had the triple test that could reduce to 1 in 6,000. Over 70 per cent of all 40-year-old women can be shown, following the triple test, to have an individual risk less than that normally quoted for a 35-year-old. But as with the AFP test, the triple test still remains a screening test. It is not a definite diagnostic test, but instead gives an indication of increased risk for either Down's syndrome or NTDs. But remember, it actually picks up only about 60 per cent of Down's cases.

As with the AFP procedure, it is worth deciding exactly why you might want to have the triple test. It doesn't put you or your baby at risk, which is a plus. But there are a lot of 'false positives' (indications of high risk which prove unfounded) in the results, and you may be one of them. You may go through a lot of unnecessary stress and heartache before finally having a healthy baby.

The triple test is done between 16 and 23 weeks, when a small amount of blood is taken from the mother. Results are usually available within around 10 days. If your risk of having a handicapped baby was thought, because of the test, to be greater than 1 in 250 (say, 1 in 100), you would 'screen positive'. One in 250 is roughly the risk of a woman of 37 having a baby with Down's. So if you come in with a lower risk ('screen negative'), the figures would look more like 1 in 500 perhaps, or 1 in 1000. It is up to you to decide if your level is one where you feel further testing is in order.

More than 9 out of 10 women will have a screen negative result, though, as we know, that does not necessarily mean that they are carrying a baby which is clear of Down's or spina bifida. But, although – as we've seen – only 2 out of every 3 Down's babies are picked up, almost all cases of anencephaly, and 4 out of every 5 of open spina bifida lesions, are identified.

The Triple Test Plus. The triple test plus has a capacity for picking up 80 to 90 per cent of Down's babies. Again, its availability in your area may be dependent on the distribution of local resources.

In a highly skilled procedure, an enzyme called alkaline phosphatase – found in white blood cells in the mother's blood known as neutrophils – is measured. Dye added to the mother's blood is specially targeted at the alkaline phosphatase, which absorbs it. The more phosphatase that there is, the deeper the colour of the dye appears. Women with Down's babies have more alkaline phosphatase present than those carrying normal babies.

At the moment, the test is too costly for wide distribution, but one of the centres that pioneered it is the University of Leeds Down's Syndrome Screening Service (telephone: 01532 344013), who have more information as to its availability.

Screening, as a first step, may be one route to take. The triple test combined with ultrasound scanning offers a combination of procedures which are the least intrusive, though of course they won't definitively pick up chromosomal disorders. But the older mother may decide that the two together give as accurate a picture as is medically possible currently without employing invasive tests. This combination of screenings gives an indication of the risk of handicap, which gives some room to decide whether it is necessary to proceed further.

Ultrasound
Ultrasound is basically the use of echoes to draw pictures. Very high frequency sound waves, which we can't hear,

are directed at and bounced off a solid object. The technique was developed to track submarines through deep water. But in this case, the solid object under investigation is the foetus, and it shows up on a small television screen like a blurred collection of many dots combining to form a well defined shadow. The sound waves reflect back in different ways, depending on the type of matter they are bouncing off. This is how it is possible to tell the difference between bone, tissue and fluid. The picture is usually in black and white, unless one of the most advanced machines is being used, and these are generally only found in teaching hospitals.

What you see is actually a series of stills which combine in super-quick succession. These are then transmitted through a computer onto a screen. It's worth knowing that the screen can be put onto hold and a polaroid taken if you want to take away a copy of the first 'photographs' of your baby.

Ultrasounds have been in use since the mid-1950s, and today almost every pregnant woman will have at least one.

The first ultrasound is usually offered between the fifteenth and twentieth week of gestation, but sometimes earlier – particularly if your hospital has a policy of having a 'dating' scan for screening tests. If it does, then it will be between 10 to 12 weeks.

If you don't want to know the sex of your baby until its birth tell the person doing the scan; they often know, and otherwise may let it slip. If you do want to know, be prepared for their getting it wrong. Twisting placentas and wriggly little penises nestling in confined spaces can confuse the issue.

You'll be asked to go for the scan with a full bladder because the extra liquid pushes the uterus upwards and makes it easier to view. If you wear a two piece for the scan, it's easy to pull up your jumper and push down your panties to allow gel to be smeared over your bare stomach – a procedure that makes for a better contact between the transducer and your abdomen. The operator then gently glides the transducer backwards and forwards over the skin, revealing the pictures on the screen as the sound waves reflect back.

The scans have many other uses. They can confirm pregnancy from about six weeks. This may seem a needless task, but for a woman who has experienced early bleeding in pregnancy it can be an immense relief to see the baby there. And for the woman who has stopped feeling all symptoms of pregnancy, the fact that the scan can show the baby's movements, including its heart beating, is reassuring.

Scans can be used to make sure the pregnancy is progressing inside the womb itself, and is not an ectopic one developing in the Fallopian tubes. And if you're having twins, or more, it can identify the number of foetuses.

They can also identify the location of the placenta. Some women have a condition called placenta praevia, which is when the placenta covers the cervix either partially or totally, and a Caesarean section would be needed for delivery. At the beginning of pregnancy many women's placentas initially appear to lie very close to the cervix, a condition known as a low-lying placenta. In the majority of cases, as the uterus grows and swells with the expanding pregnancy the placenta is pulled up and away from the cervix, leaving it clear. A series of scans are useful to ascertain whether this movement is occurring, or placenta praevia is setting in.

Some hospitals scan each pregnancy a number of times

in order to chart the baby's development and check that it is growing normally. Scans are also useful for dating pregnancy pretty accurately until about 22 weeks. Measurements are taken of the length of the baby's leg bone, the diameter of the head and the width of its tummy. There are standard growth charts to which these are then compared.

If there are concerns about the lie of the baby just before labour, scans are useful to check the position of the baby's head in relation to the mother's pelvis.

Scans can be used if other tests suggest that there may be an NTD such as spina bifida or anencephaly. They can also be used to look at the baby's bones, and especially the spine, to check for any skeletal abnormality. The heart is also usually scanned in detail.

Chromosomal abnormalities such as Down's syndrome cannot be 'seen' on the scan. But there are some physical features which can strongly indicate that it may be present. One of the identifying features of Down's syndrome is that an affected foetus will have an extra membrane at the nape of the neck, called a nuchal fold. This shows up as a black gap between the neck and the baby's back, and can be detected as early as 11 weeks. Not all doctors feel they can rely on the identification of this particular feature as a form of diagnosis. The same gap can sometimes show up on the scan of a normal baby. Three to 4 per cent of babies have the gap and the majority are normal. If one does show up, a mother may be offered chorionic villus sampling or an amniocentesis to confirm the findings.

There are limitations to the ultrasound scan. First of all, the baby itself is not always the most accommodating of subjects. It is naturally curled and furled and getting a clear view of its salient points may not be possible first time round. If you are asked to come back a second time, it doesn't necessarily mean there's a problem; it may mean that not everything was ticked off on the checklist because not everything could be seen.

If a woman is overweight it can be hard to get a clear view, so she may be asked to return.

It can depend on the abnormality, but it's thought that even expert scanners can pick up only about 70 per cent of anomalies at 20 weeks, which is the usual time it's carried out. If scans are done even earlier, at 16 weeks, that figure falls.

Some problems can develop late in pregnancy, so about 30 per cent of abnormalities remain undetected until well after birth. Renal problems in the foetus cannot be seen until about 30 weeks, when perhaps it's noticed that there is an unusually small amount of amniotic fluid.

There are conflicting reports about the risks of ultrasound. The National Institutes of Health in America in Maryland in the United States, after examining all the evidence before them, said, 'Diagnostic ultrasound is considered to be a low risk procedure. However, routine use of ultrasound in pregnancy should be discouraged.' A working party of the Royal College of Obstetricians and Gynaecologists reported in 1984 that there was no evidence of harmful physical effects from ultrasound. The implications of those two differing views are that ultrasound is extremely useful if you have a specific problem in pregnancy. You get instant information which may immediately determine the nature of care needed for you and your baby.

The real dangers seem to come from relatively unskilled people operating the ultrasound, who may transmit the wrong information. If problems do emerge, you can always ask for a second opinion, or to be referred to a regional centre which will have more powerful scanners and highly trained staff.

The 'invasive' tests

When checking for inherited genetic disease and chromosomal disorders, a sample of individual cells have to be taken from the foetus for investigation. Amniocentesis is just one of the procedures that can be used to get hold of some of these cells. Others include chorionic villus sampling (CVS) and foetal blood sampling, or cordocentesis. It's important to recognise that these three processes are three different methods for obtaining cells. They are not in themselves tests. Once the cells have been taken, then the examination of those cells can begin.

Unlike the straightforward blood test, invasive tests are not risk-free. They can induce miscarriage, and it is worth being extremely clear as to why you want the test and whether you are prepared to take the risk that goes with it.

Amniocentesis. As a procedure, amniocentesis is very simple. It's usually done between the fifteenth and eighteenth week of pregnancy, which is actually about 14 weeks from conception. (Doctors always ask for the first day of your last menstrual period simply because it's easily identifiable, and one it's assumed most women will remember. The date for conception is adjusted forward from there.)

It's important to be as clear as possible about all dates when testing. They can become quite critical. Before 14 weeks, there isn't enough fluid to safely siphon off, which is effectively what an amnio involves. But if you actually are further along in your pregnancy than you had realised, it does mean that if you do test positive, and then decide to go for a termination, you could be well advanced into your pregnancy by the time all the results are through (usually three to four weeks).

When carrying out an amnio, the doctor will use an ultrasound scan to see where the baby and the placenta are, relative to each other, within the womb. Using that image as a guide to avoid the baby, the doctor inserts a long, fine needle about four inches in length through the mother's abdominal wall into the anmiotic fluid. About four teaspoons of the fluid are then withdrawn. This amounts to less than 10 per cent of the total volume and it is replaced within a couple of hours.

In the earliest stages of pregnancy, the cells lining the amniotic sac make the liquid. But from about 12 weeks onwards, the baby begins to make its own. The baby gulps down the liquid already present and it works its way through its system. Because the liquid is travelling through the baby, it is constantly being recycled, and it contains chemicals and compounds picked up from the baby that give a true reflection of the baby's health. The baby is also periodically active, wriggling and moving about, which causes cells from its skin to fall away into the fluid. As this natural process does not produce enough cells for accurate testing, they have to be sent away to a lab and cultured for a couple of weeks so that there are more to work on. The cells are then taken out of the fluid and put under a microscope, where the chromosomes can be studied.

When carrying out the amnio, some doctors will give a local anaesthetic, though this can be more painful than the amnio itself. The whole process takes about 10 to 20 minutes.

Sometimes doctors can't get enough fluid, and may have to wait a while and then try again, though usually only once more. If there still isn't enough fluid, you should be asked to come back and repeat the amnio another day. The reason for this pause between two attempts is that there is a danger of stimulating contractions. But if you feel a mild tensing of the uterus while the test is being done, it doesn't mean contractions are beginning. It can be an automatic response which will subside once the process is over.

The test is so quick and easy it is possible to forget how monumental it may be for the woman concerned. Often, because a scan is used, it will be the first time a woman sees her baby, which can be a joyful experience for her. But because the procedure carries a very slight risk of miscarriage, the joy can be mixed with concern. If the thought of the process alarms you, ask to have the scanning screen in your line of sight. That way you can concentrate on the baby and avoid looking at the needle.

Many women are, in fact, nervous about the test beforehand. Going with a partner or friend can help. After all, intrusion into a space which is so safe and private, and yet vulnerable – because that which is inside is so precious – can put you on an instinctive, protective alert.

Once the amnio is done, and indeed before it as well, the ultrasound scan will be used to check that the baby's heart is still beating, which is reassuring. Ask for the check if it is not offered.

Some women try to make time to go home and curl up quietly after having an amnio. This is as much for them as for the baby. It can help them relax, and ease fears about adding to the risk of miscarrying. If you do notice bleeding, or leaking of the amniotic fluid from the puncture wound, ring the screening unit to let them know. If you have a slight spotting of blood from the vagina, it does not necessarily indicate the beginning of a miscarriage. It could be that a tiny blood vessel was nicked during the investigation. If your temperature rises, or you feel in any way unwell, let your doctor know immediately, as it could indicate an infection.

Once the liquid is removed, and the cell samples cultured, chromosomal abnormalities such as Down's syndrome become apparent. But the cells can also be tested for other conditions including sickle-cell anaemia and Tay Sachs disease.

The central risk associated with amniocentesis is spontaneous miscarriage. The initial danger period is thought to be within the first 48 hours, but the week after is also said to be a time of vulnerability. The risk can vary, quite simply because of the level of skill of the person doing the amnio. For that reason, you may want yours done at a hospital where amnios are done on a regular basis. You are within your rights if you ask how many times the person doing your amnio does them in a year. Any figure over 50 indicates that the person is generally well-practised in the procedure.

The risk of miscarriage from the amnio itself is probably between about 0.5 to 1 per cent, so between 1 in 100 and 1 in 200 women who have an amnio will miscarry because of the procedure. It may help to know that 4 out of every 100 women between the age of 35 and 39 will miscarry anyway, whether they choose to have amnios or not (and those figures do not include the very earliest of miscarriages, where a woman may not even be aware she is pregnant and where rates are very much higher.) It is also hard to know, if a woman is having an amnio for an already suspected abnormality, whether it was the amnio or the problem pregnancy which caused the mis-carriage.

Although it may seem to be a significant risk, it is very, very rare for the foetus to be touched by the needle. Even if it is, it is a tiny pinprick that in itself does no harm. The fact that obstetricians do 'fully sighted' amnios these days, using ultrasound to clearly identify the whole area under investigation, ensures that it rarely occurs.

Chorionic Villus Sampling. This method of testing was developed because of the length of time it takes for the results to come through from an amniocentesis. It can identify the same range of disabilities. CVS can be done at different times depending on the collection method used, but generally it is carried out at 10 or 11 weeks.

The chorion is the layer of tissues that surrounds the sac containing the growing embryo. It is covered in tiny tendrils – the chorionic villi. The tendrils on the side nearest the wall of the womb will have attached themselves, and it is this part of the chorion that busily grows into the mass of cells that becomes the placenta. Once that is established, the remaining fronds gradually recede until the tissues become smooth.

CVS samples are taken from the part of the placenta that is outside the amniotic sac. This looks much like the knotted mouthpiece of a rubber balloon. The biggest advantage to CVS is therefore that the sac itself is not punctured.

Because the chorion is made up of many living cells, any samples taken are very rich in them and in theory, they could be analysed immediately without being cultured. But there are concerns about accuracy even with the abundance of cells available, so samples generally are cultured. It can be one week, maybe two, before results are available.

Samples of cells can be removed either through the cervix, or the abdomen. Practices vary from country to country. In Britain, doctors tend to go the abdominal route. In Italy, they tend to prefer to get samples via the cervix. A woman's weight, whether she has a vaginal infection, and a number of other considerations can also determine the collection method used. The skills required are highly specialised and it's unlikely you'll find this test available outside of the big teaching hospitals.

As with amniocentesis, ultrasound scanning is used with CVS in order to determine the positions of baby and placenta, and also to pinpoint the stage of pregnancy. Having said that doctors and even nations seem to have preferences for one type of collection procedure over another, that can change in a moment depending on the position of the placenta. If it is positioned to the front of the womb, transabdominal CVS is easier. If it is towards the back, a transcervical CVS may be done. Transcervical CVS is not carried out if you are more than 12 weeks pregnant, or if you have a low-lying fibroid.

If you have a transcervical CVS, your cervix will be swabbed to make sure it is clear of infection and so prevent its introduction into the amniotic fluid. Then, while a speculum holds the sides of the vagina apart, a catheter is inserted through first the vagina and then the cervix, towards the chorionic villi which can be seen on the ultrasound screen. A tiny sample of villi are then sucked out through the catheter. If you can relax, you will feel a sensation of movement, but not pain.

Abdominal CVS is very similar to amniocentesis. Again, ultrasound is used as a visual guide and a thin hollow needle, like that used for an amnio, is inserted. It is aimed at the edge of the placenta, rather than the amniotic fluid.

As with an amnio, it may be worth going with a friend. Rest afterwards, as much for yourself as for the baby. If there is bleeding after a transcervical CVS, it's likely to be the result of the delicate vaginal walls having been disturbed, and so should not be serious. And if you've had a transabdominal, a small leakage of amniotic fluid is not unusual. But do ask for advice if you are in any way worried.

I have come across a range of figures relating to the risk of miscarriage with CVS – from 2 to 3 per cent, to a 4.6 per cent risk. What this broad range probably indicates is that because CVS itself is so new, so is the research. Also, it is carried out at an early stage of pregnancy, when there are higher rates of miscarriage anyway. So it can become harder to judge whether CVS causes the loss, or whether there would have been a miscarriage whatever the circumstances. That makes it difficult to realistically compare the risks of CVS with the risks of amniocentesis.

What seems to emerge is that amniocentesis, with its loss rate of probably 1 in 100 when carried out by the best hands, seems on the face of it to compare favourably with CVS, which has a loss rate of between 2 and 3 in every 100 procedures when carried out by the best hands. What becomes apparent, too, is the importance of the operator's experience. Experience tells. If you do have a CVS, try to make sure you have it in a large centre with people who do up to 50 procedures a year so that they are well practised. The medics themselves are well aware of how important their skill is in determining the outcome of the whole process; why shouldn't you?

When CVS was being developed, there were significant risks of defects occurring where samples were taken early on. When done at seven weeks, for example, the defects could be very serious, with whole feet and hands missing. If done at 10 weeks, the tips of the fingers might disappear. I have also heard that tongues went missing. But if done at 11 weeks on, the rate of abnormality found is the same as that occurring without intervention. Clearly, as with all tests it's essential to be as sure as you possibly can about your dates. Another disadvantage is that results can be uncertain, and may necessitate a repeat test.

Results from a CVS should be available around the twelfth to thirteenth week of pregnancy. As with an amnio, a 'normal' CVS means that the chromosomes are normal in shape, number and size. The baby's sex can be accurately determined, but there will be no information about specific gene defects unless the cell samples are tested precisely for those. Also as with an amnio, the CVS test will not pick up physical defects.

CVS has the main advantage of providing an early diagnosis. The sooner a test is done, the sooner you get the results. The results from a CVS usually arrive six to seven weeks before those of a conventionally timed amnio. So should a woman choose to terminate, the thinking behind, that is that she will find it easier to terminate earlier rather than later. Logic would seem to support that, but for many women the decision and the process seems equally traumatic at any time. And the irony of such early detection being available is that some women will go through the trauma of choosing to terminate because of abnormalities in the foetus, but may have spontaneously miscarried soon after anyway.

If early results of testing are most important to you, CVS could be the option to go for. If not, then this procedure is most useful for someone with a specific reason for having prenatal diagnosis, such as a history of handicap. If you are happy to wait longer for results and do not want invasive testing, then triple testing and ultrasound may be the route to go. If you are older and you want to have a specific diagnosis, as opposed to screening, then you might choose to have an amniocentesis.

Testing times: the way forward
The preceding pages have contained rather stark and clinical information. The fact that the mechanics of screening and testing are so cut and dried does to a certain extent distract momentarily from the tortuous emotional journey that initially thinking about the tests, then undergoing them, and finally waiting for the results can become.

Many pregnant women are concerned about testing. But it is the older mother, those women in their late thirties and forties, who perhaps have a more heightened sense of anxiety. And if you look at the figures in the table on page 250 you can understand why. A woman of 27 has a 1 in 1,000 chance of having a Down's syndrome child. By the time she reaches 35 it rises to 1 in 400, is 1 in 109 at 40, and 1 in 32 at 45. Though of course, put another way, a woman at 40 has a better than 99 per cent chance of having a healthy baby. But as we all know, if it is you who are the unlucky one, it doesn't matter much about the other 99.

Down's syndrome is a chromosomal disorder and the reason these disorders rise in relation to age has to do with the natural and unavoidable ageing of the body itself. A girl is born with exactly the number of eggs, called ova, that she will ever have. So, by the time you have got to the ripe old age of 40, so have your eggs, and they will have undergone some deterioration. The older eggs of older women do have more chromosomal abnormalities than those of younger women. But it doesn't stop there. Although the older eggs may be fertilised, their relatively deteriorated condition means they will miscarry more easily. So, even if you are ovulating and conceiving, you may very well be in that 'no-woman's-land' of sub-fertility.

For the older woman, the issues surrounding pregnancy are more numerous and in many cases more pressing than those facing her younger sisters. For instance, if the older woman has never had a child, she may have unspoken worries about fertility. In many parts of the world, a girl does not become a woman until she has a child. It is only when she has the incontrovertible proof of a live baby that she is accepted as fully matured. In the West, we have different measures and markers, and yet deep within each of us lies our instinctual nature. Whatever society ordains, for some women it is only when a baby is conceived that a primeval urge seems in some way satisfied.

Conception can take longer when a woman is older. The 'average' British couple takes six months to conceive. A quarter of all British couples take at least a year, and that is completely within the range of normal. But from the age of around 31, a woman's fertility begins to lessen. Becoming pregnant may take up to two years. And during that time the body does not stand still. The gradual lessening of fertility continues, the ovaries remain in decline.

The Catch-22 position that many older women find themselves in is that they may have tried for a long time before they conceive. As they wait, the worries about fertility increase. Is it just a temporary delay or is it, perhaps, a serious problem? Then, once she has conceived, she is faced with the dilemma of knowing that her advanced years have increased the risk of handicap, and that tests to establish the health of her baby are advisable. Wonderful though it is to at last be pregnant, the well-being of the baby is immediately put at possible risk, through miscarriage, should she do the 'sensible' thing and opt for an invasive test.

If, sadly, the baby is lost, the older woman knows that it

could take even longer to conceive next time. And the biological clock continues to tick away. The next foetus could miscarry, too – and by then they may be just the wrong side of fertility.

This is a speculative, worst-case scenario. But many older women have had time, over the years, to mull over exactly this possibility. So when it comes to screening and testing there is much to take into consideration. Many women do choose to have amniocentesis. About 60 to 85 per cent of those at risk request one. You would think that such a widespread testing of older mothers has led to a sharp decline in the incidence of Down's syndrome. But in fact, overall it has resulted in a fall of only 15 per cent in the incidence of Down's syndrome at birth.

There are a number of reasons for this. It is likely that amniocentesis is not offered to all older women. For those women who become pregnant following fertility treatment, it is possible that the thought, after such a tortuous process, of putting their baby at risk of miscarriage is unbearable. And most obviously, there may be a number of women who, when told they are having a Down's baby, do not opt for termination.

Remember, most Down's babies – 60 per cent of them, in fact – are born to women under 35. This is not just because most babies are conceived by younger women, but also because it is older mothers who are more routinely having amniocentesis (and presumably terminations), due to their being at higher risk.

If you are a 'young' older mother, and therefore in a group for whom the statistics are still relatively good, you may decide against invasive diagnostic testing. In 70 per cent of pregnancies of older women, the chances of a 40-year-old woman having a Down's syndrome child is as low as it is for a 35-year-old.

Testing, Testing: Diagnosis in the Dock

It is not a perfect system. But it is easy to forget how far testing has come and how fast. The whole battery of screening and tests that we have today were not available for our mothers. Some will say that they open a Pandora's box that would have been best left closed. The tests are a double-edged sword; but used judiciously, they can be of benefit.

CHAPTER 8

Ahead of the Game:

Preconceptual Care

You might feel virtuous, eating your greens and balancing your diet as your pregnancy progresses. But the truth of the matter is that by then it's probably too late. Careful eating and systematic exercise are essential for a healthy mother and child, but the irony is that they are most effective before conception and in the very earliest stages of pregnancy.

Our long-term health is, in fact, decided in the first four weeks of gestation. And as we know, many mothers aren't even aware they are pregnant then. Recent research is beginning to show that coronary heart disease, stroke or diabetes in later years is linked to problems with growth in the first few weeks of life in the womb. Under-nourishment, or the wrong nourishment, may programme the child to develop high blood pressure, blood clotting disorders, or abnormal glucose, insulin and cholesterol metabolism in maturity.

If the older mother does nothing else but grasp how critical those early days are, it can give her a significant head start on her pregnancy. A preconceptual care pro-gramme of healthy eating and exercise, begun a good three months (and preferably six) before getting pregnant, can produce very real benefits. For any woman worried that her advanced age already compromises the health of her baby, a well-planned programme can help balance the effects of added years. And doing something so constructive will go a long way towards allaying some of the normal anxieties that attach themselves to older motherhood.

In this chapter we will discuss, first, the research behind the theory of preconceptual care; then, an overview of nutritional needs before and during pregnancy; and finally, the issue of fertility itself – and how to control it the natural way.

INHERITED HEALTH?

For many years the medical world has been telling us to live a more healthy life. For general good health, just a bit of exercise can add zip to the day, and the right food at the right time maintains energy levels. Too much alcohol and you're wiped out the next day, particularly as you get older. Smoke a lot and you probably will not be able to run comfortably for that bus disappearing down the high street.

But new research is throwing into question just how influential any personal health programme can be if the building blocks of a healthy body are not in place before we are born. As adults we can probably tweak our general sense of wellbeing a bit here and a bit there. But a book by Professor D.J. Barker, *Mothers, Babies and Disease in Later Life* stresses that our parents' health at the time of our conception is vitally important to our own state of health.

Professor Barker studied communities living in two separate cities. Picking Edinburgh, he found people there can expect to live, on average, four years longer than their exact contemporaries in Glasgow. And that kind of seemingly unfair advantage can be found elsewhere in Britain and Europe. What is emerging is that similar people with similar lifestyles in neighbouring cities, towns and even districts have significant differences in life expectancy.

The towns of Burnley and Nelson, for example, are situated next door to each other just north of Manchester. In Nelson the adult mortality rate – the number of adults who die each year – is average for the UK. In the town of Burnley, however, the adult mortality rates are among the highest in the country. These two Lancashire towns are so similar that they don't even contain the same minor social differences that now distinguish Edinburgh and Glasgow. They have the same climate and medical services. The people of Burnley do the same kind of work as those in Nelson. They have the same income and enjoy the same recreational pursuits. But the people in Burnley die younger.

What began emerging from Professor Barker's research was that, as with Glasgow and Edinburgh, the present similarity of towns like Burnley and Nelson disguise huge historical differences.

Before the First World War, Burnley was an over-crowded industrial town and Nelson was a new one. The older houses of Burnley were back-to-backs with the usual poor ventilation and sanitation that went with them. In Nelson, the houses were newer and better placed. The streets there were cleaner, and the people living there had firm ties with the surrounding farming communities, which meant that they had both a broader sense of community and a better standard of nourishment.

The parents of the old folk now living in these two

towns thus presented very different pictures of health. And with the elderly of Burnley now dying younger than their neighbours in Nelson, it becomes clear that the legacy of ill health transmits across generations.

But there was a further mystery to the differences in death rate. Statistics from the 1960s and 1970s show that, compared with Nelson, the people of Burnley have been suffering from, among other things, higher death rates from cardiovascular disease, blocked coronary arteries and high blood pressure. Most medical textbooks still say that these diseases have nothing to do with the health of our parents. For many years we have blamed coronary artery disease on the excesses of our own lifestyles, such as our sedentary ways and liking for rich foods. But in Burnley and Nelson, adults lived, and live, the same life. Rates of smoking are the same, the intake of salt and fats are the same and so is the amount of exercise taken. So it seems that the received opinion needs to be re-examined. As Professor Barker says, it just doesn't fit the facts.

It is a known fact that cigarette smoking increases your risk of coronary artery disease. But this disease remains the most common single cause of death, even among nonsmokers; and the reason for this remains unknown. Moreover, if nonsmokers change their habits to reduce blood pressure and combat obesity, lessen their intake of fat, exercise more and so on, the expected benefits have not come their way, as a group.

In fact, coronary artery disease, worldwide, is behaving very inconsistently. It is becoming more common among the rich people in the Third World. But in the affluent West, its incidence has been falling quite markedly. There's a massive problem with obesity in America, yet there has been a surprising drop in the rate of heart disease there. Scotland, despite great improvements in health, health awareness and the general standard of living, has continued to show up poorly in the statistics.

If you tease out the facts surrounding these inconsistencies, the answer begins to emerge. It would seem that something else is causing heart disease, a factor that spares the poor of the developing world, and to some extent the rich people of the Western one. The people who seem to be targeted are the ones born into poverty, yet growing up in relative affluence. This mystery has less to do with our current 'rich' lifestyles than with the overall history of our lives. The truth of the matter, says Professor Barker, is that coronary artery disease is an illness produced by social change. More specifically, it is a disease of social improvement of a kind more commonly found in Glasgow than in Edinburgh, more in Burnley than in Nelson, and more in the UK than America: that is, social change taking place across a generation. At the individual level, this means the difference between the food your mother received – and hence her ability to nourish you in the months before and just after your birth – and the food you received when growing up.

According to Professor Barker's theory, we are programmed in the womb and during early infancy to expect a certain level of nourishment. Undernourished foetuses and infants adapt to an environment of relative starvation. This changes the balance of certain hormones, such as growth hormone and insulin, a condition which in turn produces permanent changes in metabolism. When these children grow up, become relatively affluent and are exposed to an unfamiliar high intake of fat and carbohydrate, their bodies are not geared to accept it. This difficulty in adapting is then expressed in conditions such as coronary artery disease and maturity-onset diabetes. So the die is cast much younger than we ever imagined.

For current health planners, the implications are enormous. It seems that apart from giving up smoking, changing your lifestyle in middle age makes a relatively small impact on your chances of having a first heart attack: the pathological changes began in childhood and were initiated before you were one year old. So if we really do want to reduce the immense burden of cardiovascular disease, we will need to concentrate on the nutrition of mothers and newborn infants.

The diseases we have so far considered cluster around the fatal end of the health spectrum. Obviously, we can also protect our babies from lesser forms of ill health and malady by careful attention to diet. This shouldn't be difficult: our lifestyles are supposed to be healthier than ever. A fully nourished mother anticipating having a baby of normal weight may feel, in fact, that Professor Barker's findings have little to do with her, as she is living the same well-fed life her child will and they are both programmed for health.

But is the situation this clear-cut? Many nutritionists are beginning to argue that our so called 'healthy' Western diets are anything but, as convenience and junk food contribute to forms of malnourishment usually only associated with the developing world. We need to know how best to tailor our diets to ensure the healthiest of eating patterns. The Institute of Optimum Nutrition in London is now carrying out groundbreaking research into this issue, and I spoke at length with the ION's Kate Neil about the implications for the older mother.

AN ABSORBING ISSUE

First we need to build up a physical profile of the older mother. Often, she will have had a job or career, gone out a lot for meals and drinks, and perhaps have had quite a stressful dietary history. Her digestive tract may not be in optimal health, and so her ability to absorb nutrients will have decreased. Hence she needs higher levels of nutrients than when younger, often starting at about the age of 35.

A high percentage of people now are eating a lot of allergenic food, such as wheat, dairy foods and caffeine; and, with a high sugar intake and perhaps smoking on top, these factors can irritate the lining of the gut wall and make it more leaky and less able to absorb nutrients. Diets high in sugar and alcohol can promote the excessive growth of candida albicans, the yeast-like organism responsible for causing thrush, and eventually lead to candidiasis. The candida organism can then take on a fungal form, developing a root able to penetrate the gut wall and contribute to the leakiness and poor absorption. Older women who may have been using the Pill for some time, and perhaps have had regular courses of antibiotics, are also at risk as they are often more prone to absorption problems.

How can you tell if your gut is not functioning as well as it might? Symptoms to look for include indigestion, flatulence and bloating.

Poor absorption of nutrients can go hand in hand with a build-up of toxins, which happens because the body becomes less efficient at flushing them out. And then, you start to absorb things you would be better off not absorbing. Oestrogen and cholesterol can be reabsorbed, when in fact they should be eliminated. A high fibre diet will bind with cholesterol and oestrogen, aiding their excretion.

Other toxins include those liberated during treatment for candidiasis, when the candida organisms die off. Because it is not known how such toxins, if circulating in the mother's bloodstream, would affect a foetus, it is important to treat candidiasis as part of the preconceptual care programme rather than during pregnancy. Another possible connection between candida albicans and reproductive problems is emerging. In a research project of the Institute's, on infertility, it was found that a high percentage of women diagnosed as infertile appeared to have underlying problems with candidiasis. A possible implication of the condition, then, is that cutting down on sugar and alcohol may help fertility. Overall, in fact, if there are no mechanical problems such as blocked tubes, an improved diet is a vital factor in fertility levels.

Without zinc, magnesium and vitamin A, your sex hormones cannot even be produced, let alone function. These substances are needed at every stage of the reproductive process, from menstruation right through pregnancy and birth. Zinc, for instance, is needed in the DNA molecule itself. Yet it is difficult to obtain necessary levels of zinc from the foods we eat, not least because forces outside our control, such as soil depletion, and the way food is grown, stored, cooked and transported, all leave much of what we eat depleted. So zinc supplementation is advisable, within an overall programme of vitamin and mineral supplementation.

If someone feels they may have poor absorption or candidiasis, it is worth doing a three- to six-month preconceptual care programme. It is a good idea to tackle allergies in this period, as well as improve nutrition. If a woman is allergic to certain foods, it is a good idea to sort this out before she becomes pregnant, as there is some indication that babies can react to allergic food proteins while still in utero. Allergies often tend to be familial, so sorting this out can help prevent the baby from developing similar problems.

Muscle tone, another important factor in pregnancy and childbirth, can be helped with exercise and optimal nutrition. Attention to nutrition can help prepare the body for the other stresses of pregnancy, too, such as obstructions to the flow of lymph.

It is thought that between 60 per cent and 70 per cent of babies born in the West are planned. With numbers that high, many mothers are in a position to take direct action to protect and enhance the health of their child.

FUELLING THE FUTURE: TOWARDS OPTIMAL NUTRITION

Food, sensible food

This is not a cook book; neither is it a scientific *précis* of the complexities of diet. It is, instead, a brief analysis of the way the food we eat works to keep us, and the babies we bear, fit and strong.

There is nothing quite so important when planning preconceptual care as making the best of the food you eat. With the first four weeks of gestation the most critical in the baby's development, attaining optimal health before conception means you can support the foetus in style.

The proof is that babies born at their optimum weight have the lowest risk of developmental disorders, such as those of the central nervous system. Unfortunately, around 47,000 babies are born with a low birth weight in England and Wales each year. And up to 8 per cent of them can suffer severe conditions such as cerebral palsy, mental retardation, faulty development of the lungs, blindness, deafness and epilepsy.

Striking a balance. The best preconceptual diet is balanced, varied and made up of wholefoods. If you know anything about the cooking of different cultures, one of the healthiest is found in the Mediterranean, where the focus is on the natural, the simple and the fresh. A preconceptual care diet avoids tinned and prepacked convenience foods. This means the intake of salt and additives goes down, and the intake of essential vitamins, minerals and fibres goes up.

Fresh fruits and vegetables provide minerals, vitamins and fibre which help digestion and prevent constipation. It is best to eat them raw, or lightly steamed, and without salt. It is still not clear what effect the preservatives and additives in the skins of vegetables and fruits have on the foetus so it is worth, wherever practicable, peeling or washing them.

Comforting carbohydrates. Wholegrain bread, brown rice, cereals, potatoes and wholewheat pastas are made up of carbohydrates which are an important source of energy, vitamins and fibre. They work over a long period, being digested slowly, and so release energy steadily. Thus they involve no large fluctuations in blood sugar levels, as there are with simple carbohydrates like sugar.

Positive protein. Lean meat, fish, pulses, eggs, milk, cheese, cereals, nuts and seeds make up protein. There are recommendations that pregnant women eat at least 60 grams of protein a day. The average daily intake among British adult females is 62 grams; but as this is only an average, it does mean that 50 per cent of women are eating less than this.

Fats dominate. Fats are an essential in our diet. We go into red alert at the word fat, because it names one of the biggest taboos in our society. This can mean that we turn a blind eye to the important fact that we do need fats in our diet, but of the right sort.

One of the most critical points of development for the foetus is that of the placenta, the lifeline through which all other life is delivered. If essential fatty acids are missing, growth does go on, but it is compromised: the next-best fatty acids are used instead. This could affect optimum development of the central nervous system, including the eyes. For the best health, monounsaturated fats like olive oil are needed, rather than animal and other saturated fats.

A diet too low in fats, or too rich in the wrong type, can cause a hormonal imbalance, painful, heavy periods and premenstrual syndrome in women.

It has recently been found that dietary fish oil supplements taken during the last three months of pregnancy can beneficially extend pregnancy by an average of four days. Supplementation also resulted in babies that were heavier than those whose mothers had a low fish consumption at the start of the study. Premature babies fed with milk formulas that were enriched with fish oil show faster development of the eye retina and cognitive powers than preterm infants fed on other formulas.

It's thought that gestation was prolonged because the fish oils inhibit the production of the hormone-like substances, prostaglandins, that induce labour. They're also thought to increase the production of other compounds which help to relax the uterine muscle. However, if you are planning to take extra fish oil in your diet, do check its levels of vitamin A, which in too large doses is toxic. The best way is to increase your intake of oily fish like salmon, herring, sardine, or mackerel to around three portions a week.

Calorie counting. Overall, pregnant women need an extra 70,000 calories during the whole of pregnancy to help build foetal and extra maternal tissues, fuel the mother's increased metabolic rate and provide the extra energy needed to move a heavy body around. But before you reach for the double-cream-and-butterscotch-toffee-topped chocolate sundae – a lot of those 70,000 calories can be taken from the mother's existing stores. The metabolism of pregnant women becomes more efficient and utilises all energy efficiently, rather than wasting excess as heat.

The important thing to remember is that for the first six months of the pregnancy, it is not necessary to 'eat for two'. Even more important is to avoid eating more during the preconceptual period, as weight put on then can interfere with health during pregnancy and be extra difficult to shift after. During the last three months of pregnancy, an extra 200 calories a day are needed; and while breastfeeding, an extra 450 to 570 calories.

Fabulous fibre. You can't have a healthy diet without fibre. You can't actually digest it, but that is the point. An essential component of all plant cell structures, fibre remains, indigestible in the gut, and so encourages the muscular, wavelike motion of peristalsis, which transports food through the digestive system. Along the way fibre absorbs water, toxins and bacteria. Recent research shows that dietary fibre also absorbs fats and sugars in the bowel, and can significantly lower our blood glucose and cholesterol levels, too.

We have talked about foods so far. But foods themselves have many constituent parts, and among the most important to the enquiring mother are the vitamins and minerals.

Vital vitamins

At the time of writing, I have been breastfeeding my baby for 18 months. I am taking a whole pile of vitamin supplements daily, and have done for some considerable time.

The medical world is, however, extremely divided on whether you should take vitamins. Certainly, expert advice should be taken if you do decide to go ahead with a course of mineral or vitamin supplements, because most definitely, while some vitamins should be taken at one time, others should not.

All I can report is that I can tell the days when I remember to take my pile of pills, and those when I don't. There is a significant dip in my energy: even as I breastfeed, I can feel the vitality slipping away. If I remain disciplined about taking them, my energy levels remain both good and constant. But in the end, the only thing that will really work for you is a system that you choose for yourself and which you can sustain both before conception and during pregnancy, if not after.

Vitamins are essential organic substances which have specific biochemical functions in the body. We can't synthesise enough of these substances ourselves to meet our needs, so we can only obtain them through a carefully balanced diet.

The World Health Organization (WHO) ran a study in Hungary in which either multivitamins (including folic acid) or trace elements were given to 4,000 pregnant women for at least a month before conception and a month afterwards. The women given the multivitamins were half as likely to have babies with congenital malformations as those given nothing.

Getting the right vitamins and minerals before and during pregnancy is perhaps the most significant help you can give your baby.

The cravings women have during pregnancy are legendary. But they shouldn't be mocked. They are no more than the primitive instinctive urges of the body to increase doses of certain nutrients. I remember craving grapefruit and wholemeal cucumber sandwiches, which I used to make an inch and a half high with sliced cucumber. Even then, it was only just enough. But it felt good, so I just kept on tucking in. And I'm sure it's no accident that grapefruit and cucumber are rich in vitamin C, and wholemeal bread is rich in iron.

We look at these, and the other essential vitamins and minerals, below.

Vitamin A. Found in animal products, vitamin A is fat-soluble, as it is stored in the liver. Most people eating the traditional diet of the West have enough stored vitamin A to last for about a year.

The vitamin is useful for reproduction, keeping the eyes healthily moist, good vision, the integrity of cell membranes and normal growth and development. Foods rich in vitamin A are liver, kidney, eggs, milk, cheese, yoghurt, butter and oily fish. Margarine is fortified with vitamin A by law.

Too much vitamin A can do positive harm. It can be poisonous, especially to the developing embryo. It can be associated with congenital birth defects, such as abnormalities of the kidneys and urogenital tracts. So vitamin A is usually advised against as a supplement for women planning on becoming pregnant. For the same reason, you may be advised not to eat liver. You may think you don't eat liver as a matter of course, but don't forget, pâté is made out of it.

Betacarotene. More useful than vitamin A may be various

compounds similar to it, like betacarotene, which can be found in vegetables. Unlike the vitamin A from animal products, betacarotene is water-soluble and cannot build up in the body to overdose levels, as it is flushed out through the kidneys. Betacarotene is also a powerful antioxidant (see p299).

If the body stores of vitamin A fall beyond a certain point, some molecules of betacarotene split to yield two molecules of the vitamin. But they cannot do this without zinc. So if zinc levels are low, that in itself can affect levels of vitamin A. If there is sufficient vitamin A in the body, the betacarotene stays very much as it is.

Foods rich in betacarotene are dark leafy ones like spinach and broccoli, and yellow-orange fruit and vegetables such as carrots, apricots, mangoes, red and yellow peppers and sweet potatoes.

There is no evidence that high levels are harmful to the foetus.

Vitamin B1. Vitamin B1 is essential for foetal growth. Also known as thiamin, B1 is needed for the production of energy from carbohydrates and for the synthesis of some amino acids. The amount of B1 you need depends on the amount of carbohydrate you ingest. It is common to be deficient in B1 because stores in the body are usually only enough to last a month. Those most at risk are women on weight loss diets, and those drinking large amounts of tea or coffee, both of which destroy it.

Foods rich in vitamin B1 include wheatgerm, wholegrain products, oatmeal, yeast extract, brown rice, meat, seafood, pulses and nuts.

Vitamin B2. Also known as riboflavin, vitamin B2 is needed to help smooth out metabolic processes and the production of energy, especially during pregnancy. B2 is needed in regular and consistent amounts because it is water-soluble and so not stored in large amounts.

Aside from liver, an inadvisable food in pregnancy, foods rich in B2 are yoghurt, yeast, eggs, wheat bran, green leafy vegetables, mushrooms, fruits, bread, cereals and meat.

Vitamin B3. Niacin, as B3 is also known, works on the formation of metabolic enzymes and energy production. Foods rich in niacin include lean meat, fish, poultry, yeast extract, peanuts, bran, beans, milk and wholegrains.

Vitamin B5. Pantothenic acid, or vitamin B5, while one of the lesser B group vitamins, is vital for many metabolic reactions involving carbohydrates, fats and protein. Deficiency in this vitamin is rare. The word pantothenic comes from Greek and means 'from all quarters', which describes it well, as it can be found in almost every food source.

Vitamin B6. Pyridoxine, or vitamin B6, works on over 60 enzymes and is involved in the synthesis of nucleic acid and proteins. It's particularly crucial during rapid cell division, and so is vital for the formation of red blood cells and for the growth of the foetus. It is easy to 'overdose' on B6: symptoms could include depression, headache, tiredness, bloating and irritability.

Vitamin B12. Cobalamin, as vitamin B12 is also known, works with folic acid (see below) during the synthesis of genetic material (DNA), which occurs continuously during the development of the foetus. Deficiency in either vitamin leads to the formation of cells that are larger than they should be. B12 is also instrumental in the development of healthy nerve sheaths.

Vitamin B12 is now joining its 'coworker', folic acid, as another essential for pregnant women. It has been found that neural tube defects are five times more common among babies whose mothers have low blood levels of vitamin B12, independent of their intake of folic acid.

Foods rich in B12 are fish – especially sardines – and meat, eggs, milk and cheese. It is important for vegetarians to know that no vegetables are known to contain B12. This particularly affects vegans, vegetarians who eat no dairy products. For the very strict vegetarian, ethically acceptable preparations of B12, made by bacterial fermentation, are available.

I spoke to a research nutritionist at Hammersmith Hospital in London about B12, as it is the most problematic of the B vitamins. She told me about the very latest study she had come across, which could indicate that human beings actually themselves produce enough B12 to meet their needs, independent of their diet. In the study, vegans were found to have as much B12 in their guts as meat-eaters. As a true vegan wouldn't eat foods with B12, the conclusion was that their bodies were manufacturing it.

In any case, vitamin B12 deficiency is fairly common, but this is usually caused by malabsorption from the gut, rather than dietary lack. As a B12 deficiency can lead to a failure to ovulate, it may be an undiagnosed cause of infertility. And for the older hopeful mother-to-be, who may be counting down at speed to her last ovulation, an ovulatory failure here or there is something she does not have time for.

Folic acid. The subject of birth defects is comprehensively covered in Chapter 7; so suffice it to say that an estimated 1 in 20 babies is born with a congenital malformation, and most of those born with birth defects are born to women with no obvious risk factors.

There are many forms of handicap that parents can do nothing to avoid; but some research that is emerging indicates that folic acid supplements really do have a bearing on the prevention of neural tube defects (NTDs). (The neural tube is the foetal structure that eventually develops, in the fully formed baby, into the spinal cord and brain).

If folic acid supplements are taken before and during the second pregnancy of women who have already had one child with an NTD, they reduce the risk of recurrence by 72 per cent.

A lack of folic acid is also associated with less common defects, such as cleft palate, harelip and abnormalities of the limbs, heart, lungs, skeleton and, indeed, most other parts of the developing embryo.

The governments of both the United States and the UK are so convinced of the usefulness of folic acid that they have issued specific guidelines recommending that all women planning a pregnancy take folic acid supplements. They recommend intake for three months during a preconceptual care period, and for the first 12 weeks of pregnancy. Some experts now say that pregnant women should take folic acid supplements for the full term of pregnancy, as this may guard against a baby with low birth weight and protect the mother from a type of anaemia.

Folic acid is the only vitamin whose requirement more than doubles during pregnancy. It functions in a number of ways in the body, and is involved in the formation of red blood cells, the metabolism of sugars and proteins and the formation of DNA during cell division.

The stores of folic acid in the body are limited and deficiency can set in very quickly. It is the most common of all vitamin deficiencies in industrialised countries. Symptoms include weakness, fatigue, dizziness, irritability, depression, cramps, some forms of anaemia and diarrhoea. Many commonly prescribed drugs can precipitate a deficiency.

Most of our dietary intake of folic acid comes from vegetables, bread and flour products, meat, milk and fruit. Brussels sprouts are high in it, for instance, as are spinach and green beans. Care must be taken with cooking, or the vitamin can be destroyed.

Vitamin C. This vitamin is essential for the synthesis of collagen, a protein. Collagen has recently emerged as a prime ingredient in certain types of cosmetic surgery, but in its natural form it has much to do with the formation and structure of our bodies. Vitamin C also works as an antioxidant (see p299).

Foods rich in vitamin C include blackcurrants, guavas, citrus fruits, mangoes, kiwi fruit, green peppers, potatoes, strawberries and green vegetables such as broccoli, Brussels sprouts and watercress.

A lack of vitamin C can cause scurvy, which you might think is a malady long gone from these shores. But scurvy is beginning to return, among teenage mothers. These are presumably the children who have now had well over a decade of poor nutrition and, at pregnancy, become even more seriously depleted. Many teenagers eat no fresh fruit or vegetables. I came across a report of a recent case of scurvy where a mother had been living solely on crisps, hamburgers, chocolate and cola. She developed the symptoms of bleeding gums, broken thread veins and dry, fissured lips. Paradoxically, as is often the case with malnutrition in the West, she was overweight.

Vitamin D. The absorption of calcium in the gut is aided by vitamin D. It is essential for the growth and maintenance of bones and teeth. We get most of the vitamin from the action of shortwave ultraviolet light on our skin, so our blood levels of it are naturally highest at the end of the summer and lowest at the end of winter.

As we manufacture most of our vitamin D ourselves, there is little advice about taking special supplements. It is, however, recommended during pregnancy. Foods rich in vitamin D include oily fish (sardines, herring, mackerel and salmon), tuna, fortified margarine, eggs, whole milk and butter.

A lack of vitamin D can cause poor bone development in the foetus, to a point where the skull becomes so malformed that the development of the brain is impaired, and learning difficulties may emerge later on.

Vitamin E. This vitamin functions something like a broom, sweeping away the free radicals that damage cell structure (see p299). Vitamin E protects the body's fat stores and lipid cell membranes from damage, and also protects vitamin A. Some people have suggested that vitamin E can help to prevent miscarriage and make labour easier by strengthening muscle fibres.

Foods rich in vitamin E include vegetable oils – and wheatgerm oil in particular – avocados, margarine, eggs, butter, wholemeal cereals, seeds, nuts, seafood (but not shellfish), and broccoli. Vitamin E is easily transported across the placenta. Severe deficiency can cause weakness and poor development of the heart, brain, lungs and kidneys in the foetus.

Vitamin F. A combination of essential fatty acids, vitamin F plays an important role in the formation of prostaglandins, which are crucial in fertility, conception, pregnancy and labour. Vitamin F also works in the formation of lipid cell membranes, nerve sheaths, bile, and sex hormones.

We can't manufacture essential fatty acids in large enough amounts to meet our needs, so we must get them from oily fish, nuts, seeds, unrefined oils and green leafy vegetables.

Minerals and trace elements

These tiny substances play such a large part in our health. The balance of minerals and trace elements in our diet is just as important as that of vitamins.

An imbalance of minerals and trace elements has been linked to a variety of congenital disorders. Hydrocephalus – a serious condition in which there is too much fluid in the cranium – has been associated with high levels of copper and manganese. High levels of lead and cadmium, combined with low levels of zinc, have been implicated in stillbirth. Spina bifida has been tied to low levels of zinc and of selenium.

The following minerals and trace elements are ones which you may need to take in supplements to prevent deficiency. Other minerals, such as phosphorus and potassium, are so widely available from our diet that we don't need to worry about deficiency. And trace elements not listed, such as cobalt, nickel and molybdenum, are easily obtained from a normal diet rich in pulses, wholegrains and vegetables.

Calcium. Calcium is needed during pregnancy for the growth and development of strong, healthy bones and teeth. It is also essential for muscle contraction, nerve conduction, blood coagulation, the production of energy and for the smooth functioning of the immune system. Adequate calcium intake is important throughout life, and particularly for pregnant women: poor supplies of calcium may lead to a low birth weight and slow development in the baby.

Foods rich in calcium include milk, yoghurt, cheese, green vegetables, oranges and bread. One of the quickest and easiest ways to increase your intake before pregnancy is to drink skimmed or semi-skimmed milk, which retains all the calcium of whole milk, but contains far less fat.

Chromium. Chromium is needed by the body in infinitesimal amounts – hence its classification as a 'trace element' – to help produce a compound, the glucose tolerance factor. This compound is needed to help the hormone insulin move across cell wall receptors. Low levels of chromium are evident in people with diabetes, who have poor glucose tolerance. And some experts think that low levels of its organic compound may have something to do with gestational diabetes.

The richest known source of chromium is brewer's yeast. It can also be found in considerably lesser amounts in black pepper, thyme, wheatgerm, wholewheat bread, meats and cheese. It's worth noting that most refined carbohydrates have had their chromium content removed – another good reason for eating wholefoods during the preconceptual care period.

Chromium levels are usually high in newborn babies, but decrease with age. This may reflect a dietary deficiency.

Copper. To function, the liver, brain and muscles need small amounts of copper. Copper works with brain metabolic processes, oxygen transportation and respiration. It's also essential for the production of the skin pigment, melanin, for the synthesis of collagen, and for maintaining healthy bones, cartilage, hair and skin. Copper-containing enzymes are important antioxidants (see p299).

Foods rich in copper include crustaceans, nuts, dried stone fruits, dried peas and beans, and green vegetables.

It is known that copper and zinc antagonise one another, and symptoms of copper deficiency (anaemia, low white blood cell count, subfertility, elevated blood cholesterol, thinning bones) have been seen in patients taking zinc supplements in large amounts for over a year. The Pill can cause copper levels in the blood to increase and zinc levels to decrease. If you are taking supplements, balancing amounts of copper and zinc might be an advisable, if complicated, exercise.

Iodine. Thyroid hormones are synthesised by iodine. In the foetus, this is a vital process that occurs during the first three months, when it is part of the chemistry influencing the development of the central nervous system.

Foods rich in iodine include marine seafoods such as shrimp and lobster, seaweeds and iodised salt. Because cattle feed is iodised, cow's milk is also a good source. It is rarely seen in this country, but iodine deficiency can lead to hypothyroidism in babies, a condition also known as cretinism, which is characterised by physical and mental retardation.

Iron. A constituent of haemoglobin – the protein in red blood cells which carries oxygen from the lungs to the tissues, and carbon dioxide back to the lungs for excretion – iron is also needed during the combustion of food with oxygen to produce energy and water. During pregnancy, the mother's red blood cell mass increases by 30 per cent, and relatively large amounts of iron are needed to service it. Iron also helps the foetus develop its own blood stores.

Foods rich in iron include red meat, poultry, fish, nuts, wholemeal bread, cocoa, egg yolk, green vegetables and parsley. Overcooking can decrease the amount of iron in vegetables by up to 20 per cent. When eating iron-rich foods, it is useful to take some vitamin C on board too, as this improves absorption. Calcium and tannin-containing drinks, such as tea, decrease it.

Magnesium. Magnesium is needed for every major biological process, from the synthesis of protein and DNA to glucose metabolism, energy production and enzyme function. It is essential for healthy tissues, including heart, muscle and nerve cells.

Nuts, seafood, seaweeds, soya beans, meat, eggs, milk, dairy products and wholegrains are all rich in the mineral. Chlorophyll, the green pigment in plants, contains magnesium, so green leafy vegetables are a good source too. Magnesium deficiency is common. Symptoms include poor appetite, tiredness, insomnia, constipation, muscular spasms, twitches and cramps. A lack of magnesium can be made worse by pregnancy, and some researchers believe a deficiency can contribute to miscarriage, premature delivery, and painful contractions during childbirth.

Manganese. An important antioxidant (see p299), manganese is more of a mystery mineral than the others: its main functions are not known. It is thought to be important in the synthesis of blood clotting factors and cholesterol, and is also involved in brain physiology, particularly the synthesis of the neurotransmitter dopamine. Lack of manganese is linked to reduced fertility, poor foetal growth, birth defects and stillbirth in animals.

Manganese-rich foods include wholegrains, nuts, fruits, seeds, yeast, eggs, and leafy green vegetables and herbs. Tea is an exceptionally rich source of manganese, and it's thought that half of our daily intake comes from drinking it.

Selenium. Like manganese, selenium is a powerful antioxidant (see below). It is also essential for cell growth and in fighting infection, but is only needed in minute quantities. It works alongside vitamin E.

Broccoli, mushrooms, cabbage, radishes, onions, garlic, celery, fish, wholegrains, wheatgerm, nuts and yeast contain selenium.

Selenium deficiency has been identified as an important feature in cot death. In the United States, a quarter of babies who die from sudden infant death syndrome were found to be deficient in selenium and/or vitamin E. Most of them had been bottle-fed rather than breastfed.

Zinc. This mineral performs a multitude of tasks. It's an important cofactor working alongside over a hundred different enzymes, and forms an integral part of one enzyme, which 'switches on' human genes in response to a hormone trigger. Zinc is vital in the development of the foetus. Its role in the immune system is important, as is its capability of preventing age-linked degeneration of vision.

Oatmeal, wholegrain products, yeast, seafoods, meat, nuts, milk, eggs, and cheese are all good sources of zinc.

A woman's blood levels of zinc fall by around 30 per cent during pregnancy. This level remains constant whether she is taking supplements, or not. Zinc levels in the foetus are usually double those of the mother's.

Antioxidants and free radicals

A number of the vitamins and minerals we've considered so far have been listed as antioxidants. The term 'free radicals' has also popped up. What are they?

Free radicals are highly unstable entities that move around the body, attacking its natural processes and causing damage to proteins, fats, cell membranes and DNA. In chemical terms, free radicals are molecular fragments that carry a negative electrical charge. They move about, colliding into other molecules, in an attempt to neutralise themselves either by stealing a positive charge or offloading their own negative one. This process is known as oxidation.

It's thought that every cell in our body is subjected to 10,000 oxidations by free radicals every day. Our main line of defence against these attacks are antioxidants, which clear up the free radicals by neutralising their negative charge before they can cause harm.

Some of the factors that lead to the formation of free radicals can be eliminated from our lives; some can't. These include normal metabolic reactions, cigarette smoke, exhaust fumes, X-ray irradiation, UVA rays from the sun, and alcohol and drugs, especially antibiotics.

The damage to cells' lipid membranes and fat stores by free radicals can lead to premature wrinkling of the skin. Oxidation of cholesterol hastens furring and hardening of the arteries leading to coronary heart disease. If the genetic template of DNA in each cell's nucleus is oxidised, errors can occur when chromosomes are duplicated during cell division. This can ultimately affect future cell division. And if DNA in the sperm or ova are damaged by oxidation, there are several undesirable outcomes.

The damaged sperm or egg may be incapable of fertilisation. Or damaged genes may be passed on to the developing foetus, if fertilisation is successful. The baby may then develop a congenital birth defect, or may grow slowly and be small for dates. The growing child may develop a cancer, or may themselves pass on genetic defects to future generations with unpredictable consequences.

So the importance of combating free radicals is self-evident. A judicious mix and intake of the right combination of antioxidant vitamins and minerals can be extremely beneficial during the preconceptual period.

This is especially the case for men, whose sperm take around 74 days to fully develop. Women's egg cells are present from birth. But two important egg cell divisions occur at the time of ovulation, and again at fertilisation, so although long-term protection against free radicals may have been difficult to maintain consistently, at this particularly vulnerable time it is worth keeping up the levels of antioxidants to maintain a safe environment. And antioxidants obviously play a significant part in pregnancy, when the billions of chromosomal replications of rapid cell division are happening, and making the baby grow.

Smokers and people with diabetes need twice as many antioxidant vitamins as other people, as they generate many more free radicals. They should take vitamins C, E, and betacarotene in high doses before and during pregnancy.

The right combination
It can be bewildering to think out how to combine all the necessary ingredients into the right package in order to deliver exactly the required doses in the right place at the

right time. For it is just as important to remember that too high an input of vitamins and minerals can be as dangerous as too little.

Finding the balance is complicated by the fact that there are two schools of thought about supplementation of diet. One says that it is pointless, as a healthy balanced diet will give you all that you need. They say that adding to a good diet is a waste of time, effort and money. The other says that supplementation is essential. A 'healthy diet' is increasingly hard to organise on a daily basis, given our busy lifestyles, and the fact that the foods we buy are full of preservatives, additives and antibiotics. With meat, you can also include growth promoters in the list and, in the case of fish caught in the North Sea, you can add nuclear waste. It is not a pretty thought.

At the end of the day, we have to rely on our own knowledge and inclination to decide whether to use supplements. But we should remember that pregnancy is not an average time. Huge changes are wrought on the mother's body and huge demands made of it. Research is proving the efficacy of shoring up reserves at a time of depletion and overextension, which is indeed very much what producing a baby is all about. For the older mother who has the time to prepare for her child's conception, a few months of preconceptual care could help compensate for her added years.

If you do wish to embark on a comprehensive nutritional programme as part of a preconceptual care plan, it is important to get expert help. Your needs and circumstances are unique and what may be appropriate for the next mother-to-be may not be appropriate for you.

There are so many things that a woman cannot control about her reproductive experience, but diet is not one of them. And luckily, diet is one of the single most important factors that can affect the health of the mother, the embryo, the foetus, the baby, the child.

CYCLING FOR BEGINNERS: EXPLORING OUR OWN FERTILITY

Optimal nutrition is one way of boosting fertility and making healthy pregnancies and babies more of a probability and less of a game of chance. Another highly important factor in preconceptual care is perhaps even more basic: getting to know your own body, and in particular your ovulation cycle. This, in turn, can help you sort out with fair precision the times when you are most fertile.

Time is running out for the older mother-to-be. Each fertile cycle is precious and could indeed be the last. For a woman who wants a child the pressure to conceive increases enormously the nearer to menopause she gets. It is tantalising to know your days as a fertile woman are numbered and yet not know by how many. It's a little like shadow boxing with a hand tied behind your back. An understanding of the subtleties of female physiology can make all the difference between success and failure.

Back to basics: reproductive physiology

From the moment we're born, our bodies start to prepare for our fertile years. At birth we have two million egg-forming cells in our ovaries. Which is just as well, because most of those follicles, as they're called, are already long gone by the time puberty starts. By then, there are around 40,000 left.

No new ones are ever produced.

Puberty usually begins in the early teens, triggered by the young girl's newly functioning 'female' hormones. A few follicles begin to ripen every month.

A hormone is simply a natural chemical compound, made and released by a variety of glands around the body, creating automatic physical responses wherever it is sent. The brain sends out the order. The hormone carries the message. The targeted part of the body does what it's instructed to do. From this comes the rhythm of our cycles.

Understanding the ebb and flow of hormones as they trigger changes in the ovaries, uterus and cervix can help a lot in planning preconceptual care. This rhythm is very different for each of us. For some women, the menstrual cycle lasts 21 days, or even less. For some, as many as 50 days can elapse between the start of each period. Both are normal. Only 12 per cent of women have the 'usual' 28-day cycle. The only thing that seems to remain constant for all women is that ovulation, if it happens, is at 14 days, plus or minus one, before their next period starts.

Most women are conscious, to some degree, of the outward, physical aspects of their cycle. The cervical mucus changes, the endometrium swells and the ovarian follicle begins to develop. But the true start takes place near the brain.

The road to ovulation. Nestling in a small bony cavity at the base of the brain is the pituitary gland, a round, pealike piece of soft tissue. The pituitary releases a hormone called follicle-stimulating hormone, which quite literally tickles the egg-forming cells in the ovaries into action. When follicle-stimulating hormone is released, 10 to 20 follicles begin to ripen.

Next, the ovary swings into action. The ovary is not just a storehouse of potential eggs. It, too, is a gland in its own right. As the follicle develops, the ovary begins to manufacture and secrete oestrogen. So, at the beginning of the cycle, the levels of oestrogen in the blood begin to rise. And at first, ironically, that oestrogen begins to work as a temporary block, stopping the pituitary gland producing any more of its follicle-stimulating hormone. This is called negative feedback.

The ovaries continue to produce even more oestrogen. And now, as the levels of oestrogen go up, the pituitary suddenly starts up again and goes full steam ahead to compensate. This time the pituitary gland releases a new compound, called luteinising hormone, plus some more follicle-stimulating hormone. This return volley is called positive feedback.

Somehow, this to-ing and fro-ing all works together to culminate in a neatly judged crescendo. Because after all that activity, the luteinising hormone does what it's meant to do: it triggers ovulation. An egg is released.

In the ovaries, all of the stimulated follicles are prepared, in anticipation. Each one has the potential to grow. But only one will be chosen. And the luteinising hormone is particularly clever. It will isolate the biggest and the best. In fact, that particular follicle will actually be visible to the naked eye. The hormone will then encourage the follicle, which will be blown up tight like a tiny balloon, to burst away from the ovary and make its journey to the womb via the Fallopian tubes. So begins the survival of the fittest.

As a rule, in humans only one egg is released each month. Contrary to popular belief, an egg is not released from each ovary on alternate months. There doesn't seem to be a pattern; eggs are released from the two ovaries in an irregular and unpredictable sequence.

The Fallopian tubes are wrapped round the ovary. The inside surface of each tube is covered with tiny hairlike projections called cilia, which beat repeatedly to set up an eddy of currents. These suck the newly released egg into the tube and then carry it downwards on what has been described as the ciliary escalator. Fluid currents and contraction of the walls of the Fallopian tubes also aid the egg on its downward journey.

It's not known how long the egg remains fertilisable within the tube, but it is probably for only a short period – around one day. If it isn't fertilised, it starts to degenerate.

That is ovulation: the liberation of the ripened follicle from the ovary. At this point a woman is at the optimum point of fertility in her cycle.

The falling away. Meanwhile, other parts of the cycle are still unfurling. Back in the ovary the empty follicle turns into what is called the corpus luteum, or yellow body, and that produces yet more of the hormone oestrogen, plus the other female hormone, progesterone.

In the first half of the menstrual cycle, oestrogen worked on building up the lining of the womb. In the second half of the cycle, the progesterone joins in. The lining – the sponge-like endometrium – grows thicker. Progesterone also stimulates the lining of the womb so that it secretes a nutritious mucus in preparation for possible conception.

If there is no conception, the corpus luteum dies. The hormone levels change. And the endometrium falls away. Part of the endometrium's function is to collect as much blood as possible, to provide the healthiest environment for the baby. When the lining goes, the blood goes too, and we get a monthly bleeding or period.

The time this usually takes is, like the lead-up to ovulation, 14 days – hence the 'average' 28-day spell between periods. This gap will change with age, however.

When a young girl starts her periods, her cycle will often be around 35 days. That cycle then gradually condenses until her early forties, when it begins to expand again, to about 50 to 52 days. And at that time she will have about eight thousand follicles left, only a few of which will ripen.

Women in the later stages of their fertile life produce more follicle-stimulating hormone than they did when younger. But even so, ovulation doesn't happen at every cycle and without it, no progesterone is made either. So overall, the production of progesterone and oestrogen begins to dwindle. Menopause is beginning.

The clock winds down. The question of when menopause begins, one of the most fundamentally important to the older mother, is difficult to answer for many women. Some women's menopause begins at 37, others start in their forties or early fifties. Yet the biological clock is inexorable, and a time will come to all women, if they live long enough, when they are no longer fertile. It is just that the journey each woman takes to that point is unique. Her menopausal indicators will combine to form a very individual physical, temperamental and emotional picture.

What we do know is that for many women the process takes time, spreading itself over a number of years. Some women experience only one or two classic symptoms, like hot flushes or night sweats from time to time, and their menopause passes quite easily. Others find it much more difficult, suffering many of the symptoms simultaneously and for a protracted time.

The exact point at which menopause begins remains elusive, however. Your gynaecological history will not necessarily mimic your mother's, and in any case offers no clues to when your fertility will really end. It is not surprising that women have been known to panic about the ticking away of the biological clock. There is nothing so stressful as having to make hard and fast decisions about when to have a child, when one of the most important facts that will affect that decision is unknown.

One of the central problems of older women in this position is 'subfertility'. As menopause approaches, there are some months when ovulation fails. This is called an 'anovulatory' cycle, and the chances of getting pregnant during it are nil.

During such a cycle, no corpus luteum is produced. That means that no progesterone is secreted, which is necessary for the next phase of the menstrual cycle. Oestrogens from the ovary continue to be released, so the expansive growth usually associated only with the first part of the cycle simply continues. Eventually, the endometrium becomes thick enough to outgrow its blood supply, and starts to spontaneously break down without the stimulation of hormones. As it degenerates, it triggers a menstrual bleed. The time it takes for bleeding to occur is variable, but is usually less than 28 days from the onset of the previous period. The bleeding itself will vary from scanty to profuse.

Only those alert to changes in the mucus discharged from the cervix will be able to distinguish between a barren or fertile cycle. Throughout a normal cycle, this mucus goes through several permutations. During the first part of the cycle, oestrogen encourages the production of thin and alkaline mucus, which is ideal for the survival and easy penetration of the sperm. The cervical mucus becomes increasingly fluid, slippery and elastic until ovulation occurs. At this time, a drop of cervical mucus can be stretched into a thin thread up to six inches long. The molecules in the mucus are well aligned and it is easy for sperm to swim through.

Within days of ovulation, when progesterone is being produced, the cervical mucus suddenly changes in texture. It becomes inelastic, and the molecules are now entangled into a tight web, making it increasingly impenetrable. It now looks thick, sticky and scant, and is moreover hostile to sperm.

For the older woman who knows her fertile days are numbered, recognising a fertile cycle could be invaluable. They may be diminishing in number, and the more easily and speedily she can identify them, the more she can capitalise on them.

It is true that some couples trying for a baby like to forget about the pressures of time and just trust to nature, good health and good luck. That is in fact often the advice given to people experiencing initial difficulties with fertility: the less you think about it, the less tense you are, and the less tense you are, the more likely you are to conceive. But for the woman in her forties, hedging her bets may feel safer. A firm grasp of the signs and indications of fertility, through a method called 'Fertility Awareness', can help.

Peak practice: cultivating Fertility Awareness
It is ironic that what is a form of natural contraception for many can be and is used to aid conception. Fertility Awareness is exactly as it sounds: a detailed understanding of your own ovulation cycle. Once you can identify it, you can exploit that short window in time when you are at your most fertile. Fertility Awareness, also called the symptothermal method, has replaced the older, and less reliable, so-called rhythm method.

First we'll look at an overview of fertility through the cycle.

The first, relatively infertile phase starts on the first day of bleeding and ends when the follicles in the ovaries start to mature. Not only does this differ in length of time from woman to woman, but from cycle to cycle too. Though it's unlikely, you can still get pregnant at this time.

The fertile phase extends from the start of the follicle development until 48 hours after ovulation. Remember, for most women ovulation occurs 14 days before the beginning of the next period. So if your cycle is 21 days, you'll ovulate on day 7; if 35 days, on day 21.

The post-ovulatory, or second infertile phase, lasts from 48 hours after ovulation until the start of the next menstrual period. This can vary from 10 to 16 days, with an average length of about 13 days. The post-ovulatory phase, also known as the absolutely infertile phase, is virtually guaranteed not to result in pregnancy.

So a woman's peak period of fertility is a very short spell in each cycle. Sperm can survive in the womb for three to five days. But successful fertilisation usually occurs within 12 to 24 hours after ovulation. So it seems most sensible to introduce the sperm sooner, rather than later.

Fertility Awareness works as follows. You judge when you are ovulating by taking body temperature readings morning and night, on a daily basis, and plotting them on a graph. These will show, as do changes in vaginal mucus, when the cycle is peaking. At ovulation, body temperature drops slightly and then rises by 0.2 to 0.4 degrees Centigrade. It stays high until the next period starts. The second infertile phase of the cycle begins on the morning of the third consecutive high reading, after the temperature shift that occurred at ovulation. Be aware that you must watch out for infections. They cause temperature rises which can mask or mimic ovulation.

Getting to grips with the method does require constant vigilance, and it may be worth getting in touch with a family planning clinic for more detailed advice, and information on courses (see p330). But with practice, a sense of super-alertness sets in, and it becomes easier and easier to ready body signals.

One piece of advice I came across when talking about older mothers to a nursing sister who works in a family planning clinic made a lot of sense. 'Make love earlier in the cycle,' she said, 'rather than right on top of what you think is the time of ovulation. Sometimes you ovulate early, and as sperm live longer than an ovum, if it is already in place when you ovulate you've got a greater chance.' This goes slightly against Fertility Awareness, which indicates you should be sure ovulation is starting. But a judicious mix of the two could work.

Another potentially useful adjunct to the method is the ovulation predictor kit, which can be used to pinpoint when you ovulate with greater accuracy.

But temperature and changes in vaginal mucus are not the only indicators of fertility scrutinised when following the method. Keeping charts and detailed records of the following signs can significantly enhance its accuracy.

- Mood changes, which often occur two weeks before a period is due.

- The position and texture of the cervix, which becomes softer, opens and rises higher in the vagina during the fertile phase (although these changes are less easy to detect once you have a child).

- A mid-cycle show of blood or pink-stained mucus.

310

- Mid-cycle pain, occurring 24 to 48 hours prior to ovulation. Called Mittelschmerz, this pain is caused by a distension of the ovarian capsule as it swells before ovulation. Recent research indicates that a woman experiencing Mittelschmerz will start her second infertile phase five days later, if her temperature/cervical mucus chart is in sync.

- Breast sensitivity.

- Acne and other skin changes.

If the method's complexity puts you off, and you don't want to structure your attempts to conceive quite so consciously, a broad understanding of the general interplay of these signs and symptoms can certainly put you on the right track.

Considering contraception
Contraception is obviously vital to preconceptual care. While boosting your levels of nutrients and getting to know your body, you may actively not want to get pregnant. But equally, you may want to avoid any method of contraception that lessens your chances of conceiving later.

Fertility Awareness is an ideal method of contraception for the preconceptual care period, as it has no side effects. Neither do the barrier methods, such as the male condom, the female condom, the diaphragm, spermicides or the sponge. But if you are already using the coil, you might want to consider stopping it, and switching to one of those more natural methods for the duration of your preconceptual care period. The facts surrounding the Pill are less clear-cut.

The coil has a number of effects on the womb and works in several ways to prevent pregnancy. The obvious one is of physical interference with implantation. The coil can also cause low-grade inflammation of the endometrium with infiltration of white pus cells (leucocytes). It stimulates the production of hormone-like prostaglandins. The copper that the coil is made of produces ions that are toxic to ova and spermatozoa. And it interferes with the transportation of sperm and egg within the Fallopian tubes. Given all this, it would be advisable to remove the coil at least three months before attempting conception.

The Pill also works in a number of ways to stop conception. It inhibits the secretion of follicle-stimulating hormone and luteinising hormone from the pituitary gland. As we know, without these the ovarian follicles cannot mature each month, and ovulation stops. The Pill thickens the cervical mucus so that sperm cannot easily swim through. It thins out the lining of the womb, so that if an egg does become fertilised, it cannot implant or develop. The transportation of sperm and eggs in the Fallopian tubes is slowed.

When the Pill first came on the market, there was much alarm that it would affect women's long-term fertility. But in general that is a concern that remains unproven. A look at a number of studies with differing outcomes will, however, give us a fuller picture of the Pill's effect on fertility.

Some studies suggest that, among previously fertile women who stop using the Pill in order to conceive, 90 per cent delivered a child within 30 months (This is similar to the figures for women who had been using the diaphragm or coil). A delay of two to three months in the time taken to conceive was noted in these women. But it was thought that this was caused because they had been following preconceptual advice not to conceive straightaway after coming off the combined Pill.

Those statistics seem on the face of it to bode well. But we do need to look at further research, which has implications for the older mother in particular. It was found, in another study of what were termed 'older', childless women between 30 and 35, that they experienced a more marked delay when trying to conceive after coming off the Pill. Fifty per cent of these women took a year longer to get pregnant than women of the same age who had not been on the Pill but had been using a diaphragm. Eventually, conception rates between the two groups did even out, and were almost identical after 72 months, suggesting that there was no permanent impairment to fertility.

However, few women – and much less, their older sisters – want to wait six years once they start trying to have a family. More to the point, this study only looked at 30- to 35-year-old women. There have been no similar studies on women older than this, but one cannot assume that the figures get any better. Logic would indicate that for those 50 per cent it would, if anything, be the reverse.

Other evidence, from a 1980s study by the World Health Organization, does little to dispel this gloomy picture. While it stated that the use of the Pill before conception had no detrimental effects on the developing foetus, the study did express anxieties about altered vitamin and mineral levels in the mother, which it felt could lead to reduced fertility and have an impact on the foetus.

The changes in the mother's levels of nutrients in the bloodstream have been the subject of a number of other studies. For instance, levels of vitamin A can actually go up for around three months after the Pill is first prescribed. This would seem a good thing, as normal levels of vitamin

A play a vital role in limb development in the foetus. But, as we know, too much can lead to abnormalities. And as it takes three months for vitamin A levels to return to normal after coming off the Pill, it might be sensible to stop in good time.

The Pill lowers levels of vitamins B1 and B2 in the blood by making it harder to metabolise. But there is disagreement about B6. Some studies seem to prove that levels lower, others that they are unaffected.

Folic acid, vitamin B12, vitamin C and vitamin E are all affected by the Pill. Anyone becoming pregnant within three months of stopping the Pill is advised to increase their intake of these in their diets.

Levels of iron may actually rise because the Pill causes lighter bleeding, and less haemoglobin is lost. The Pill is also thought to increase levels of copper, which is not necessarily a good thing, as it is known to be a contributing factor in high blood pressure during late pregnancy, and postnatal depression.

Zinc is perhaps the most important mineral that can be affected by the Pill. The Pill is known to change a woman's capacity to absorb zinc, and this could be critical if she is trying to get pregnant, as zinc deficiency has been linked to subfertility. Zinc is also, as we have seen, vital in the development of the foetus.

Having said all this, there is some evidence that dramatically counterbalances the image of the Pill as an undesirable in the preconceptual care plan. It has been found that some women hit an extraordinarily high peak of fertility soon after stopping the Pill. That is why the Pill is actually used to help prepare some women who are about to undergo assisted fertility techniques.

It was discovered by chance in one study that successful pregnancy rates were twice as high in women given the combined Pill before *in vitro* fertilisation, compared to those not taking the Pill. In the study, the women had been given the Pill to ensure they were at the correct point in their menstrual cycle when specialists carried out the treatment. It is hard to know if it was simply the technique of precisely timing and identifying the moment of peak fertility that led to such success in the laboratory, or whether something intrinsic to the Pill really does lead to a brief hyper-fertility when the body is suddenly released from it. Whichever it is, it would be a shame to waste this prime window of opportunity should it happen to you.

Should you come off the Pill? It is impossible to know beforehand whether you will experience a long delay in conceiving, or hit that blast of peak fertility and conceive easily and almost immediately. But it is hard to think that some women in their late thirties or early forties may have a six-year wait. While the choice is ultimately up to you, the chance that you might be one of those women would seem to indicate that switching to a natural form of contraception as part of your preconceptual care regime is a good idea. And this view is bolstered by the fact that the Pill can play havoc with nutrient levels in the body, a balance of which is so vital in preconceptual care.

EPILOGUE

Eating well and staying fit and healthy is money in the bank for the older mother. More and more women are delaying motherhood, or adding to their families in their late thirties and early forties. There are some hurdles that the older mother may be more likely to come across than a younger one. But knowing that, she can do much to prepare herself in the best possible way.

The older mother is now so firmly established on the graphs and statistical breakdowns that she is no longer the curiosity she once was. The obstetric and gynaecological environment is changing at great speed all around her, as is the world in general. She needs to be aware of the currents and attitudes that could shape and influence her experience.

As modern science opens Pandora's box ever wider, the world of medicine has a part to play in her life as never before. With some prescience Professor Kypros Nicolaides of King's College Hospital London has said, 'The barrier between the foetus and the obstetrician is being shattered. Now that we have access to the foetus, the philosophy of the foetus as patient is emerging.' The barrier the Professor

316

talks about is, of course, the mother. It is older mothers as a group who have more investigations than most into the health and viability of their unborn babies. This is a shift in prevailing obstetric care that they might be wise to note.

More positively, the deeply ingrained prejudice about the older mother being unfit to bear a healthy child may gradually be losing its iron grip. That is because more and more pregnant women of *all* ages could soon be having routine serum screening for foetal abnormality (blood tests to you and me). The implications of this are that there may be a change in pregnant women's perceptions about advanced age being the sole factor that increases the risk of Down's.

In terms of percentages there are comparatively fewer older mothers than younger ones, and within their smaller group it is always going to be the case that older women are more likely to screen positive than younger ones. But just in terms of volume there will be greater numbers of younger women screening positive with possible foetal abnormalities. Conversely, the same routine blood tests will screen out many older women, proving at this first test that their babies are most probably normal. So, large numbers of older women will be seen to be free of this dilemma. Eventually, age alone may not be seen to be the sole major risk factor that it currently is. Common perceptions may change, and it will be more generally recognised than it is now that younger women, too, can conceive children with Down's.

Postmenopausal motherhood is now very much on the agenda. There was a terrific uproar in this country at the beginning of the 1990s when Professor Antinori from Rome successfully helped a British woman of 59 become pregnant via egg donation. But the truth of the matter is that the same work had been, and clearly still is, quietly going on in Britain. At the time the story broke, at least 15 other postmenopausal women had been successfully delivered of their babies in the UK. These mothers are extremely rare, but their numbers will increase. And as with most things, we probably will get more and more used to it with time.

For the older woman hoping for a child the central problem remains that the eggs she has now are the eggs she was born with. As Dr Gill Lockwood, the clinical research fellow in infertility at the John Radcliffe Hospital, said to me so trenchantly, 'Little girls are born with every egg they're ever going to have, and you wouldn't buy an egg from Sainsbury's if it had been on the shelf for forty years, would you? Why should you expect to make a healthy baby from it? But people do.'

Theoretically, one solution could be for a woman to have some of her eggs extracted and stored when she is younger and the contents of her ovaries are at their healthiest. But at the moment it is not possible to successfully freeze eggs taken from a human being. An egg is very much like a bubble. It has a very thin skin and a huge, fluid-filled space in the middle. Ice crystals are formed and it shatters when frozen.

But we can freeze embryos. So the scenario that some fertility experts are envisioning is that if a woman has found the man she wants to be the father of her children by her twenties or early thirties, she could start 'planning' her family then. If this hypothetical couple want children, but not for some years, they could undergo IVF using her healthy young eggs and his sperm. The viable embryos that result could be frozen and kept for a later date.

One doctor saw it thus: 'She then gets to be chairman of the board, and when she's finally forty-fiveish and mature and ready to take early retirement and to enjoy motherhood, she has her own embryos replaced. She faces no greater risk of Down's or miscarriage, the two most serious physical conditions for the older mother to consider, because it's the age of the eggs that critically affects those two things, not the age of the woman. She could theoretically go on "implanting" until she was sixtyish.'

Dr Lockwood outlines something even more futuristic. 'What is more likely to happen,' she says, 'is something that has already been successful in animals. That is to freeze little biopsies of ovary, when they are at the primordial follicle stage, tiny and invisible to the naked eye. Then, when you want to use those biopsies to do your IVF, you simply thaw out the minute fragments of ovarian cells that make up the biopsies and graft them back into what has become a postmenopausal ovary. That implantation would stimulate the surrounding ovary, which would then become *pre*menopausal again. You could effectively reverse the woman's menopause. It would be the ultimate hormone replacement therapy! But this is getting into the realms of science fiction. In a hundred years' time, that's what will happen, if we are still here.'

Back here in the present, one last configuration of interest to the older mother is a relatively new departure in egg donorship: the surrogate granny. This development has already happened in other parts of the world. But medical history was made in Britain when 49-year-old Edith Jones became the first British woman to be implanted with two embryos formed from her daughter's eggs and her son-in-law's sperm. At the time of publication she is pregnant and waiting to give birth, effectively, to her own grandchildren. Her daughter Suzanne, who is 20, was born without a womb. Mrs Jones has said, 'I am doing it for Suzanne and for no other reason. If you have children you do anything to help them.'

Although Mrs Jones began the menopause five years ago, doctors believe there is a good chance of success because the embryos are from a young couple. Apparently grave reservations have been voiced about the emotional problems the young child could face, with some family campaigners describing the whole idea as 'bizarre'.

Bizarre it may be. But is it wrong? If there is love, if there is care, if there is nurturing, as there clearly is in this case, who is to say these babies have no right to life? And also, who is to say these women have no right to conceive or bear them in any way possible?

Edith Jones will be a name that, like Louise Brown, will become a common byword for yet another extraordinary leap in reproductive science. She has set a precedent in this country by embarking on a pregnancy which means she will deliver her grandchildren from her own body. She certainly qualifies as a vintage mother.

Good luck to her. Good luck to her children, and good luck to her children's children.

THE CHILDREN

This book is first and foremost about the realities of being an older mother. A number of them have spoken, sometimes with devastating frankness, about how having a child in middle age has changed their lives. But so far we have not heard the other side. What does it mean to be the child of 'older' parents? Are you marked for life – or is it just another thread woven into a rich tapestry?

Jon, 17

I was planned. My mother had got pregnant by accident many years after she'd had what she thought was her last child. But she miscarried. She was so upset that she decided to try again immediately even though she was over 40.

For as long as I can remember, my brothers and sisters have treated me like an adult. They never babied me. And always talked to me about things as if I was their age, instead of 10 or 12 years younger. But when I was around 10 they used to pick on me a lot and I can remember crying till they told me I should learn to put up with having the mickey taken.

Having older brothers and sisters has made me more responsible, I think. When my friends come over I'm always watchful about them treating the house right and not breaking things.

We're all very close, but because I'm at home from time to time I've seen my parents hurt or annoyed over something one of my older brother or sisters has done, like not getting in touch enough. I'm going to make sure I never do that to them once I've left home.

One of the best things about the way I've been brought up is the time my parents have given me. I've always felt they've enjoyed my company and they respect me. They do expect quite a lot. But I don't mind. I've had so many people taking an interest in me. I've felt very secure, and I haven't had to fight for attention.

Mick, 18

Even though I've got two older sisters I've always felt like an only child. They seem more like aunts than anything. I suppose I've missed out in some ways, not having brothers and sisters my own age. But I make friends easily, so I've made up for it.

I think if I had a younger brother or sister I'd've been jealous. I do know that I have had a cushy life having Mum to myself. She's made my life easy. She's very liberal. And far more understanding than other parents I know. My friends all think she's great. But she doesn't always understand my generation as well as she thinks.

My sisters think I've had it cushy. The younger one still resents that she had to do so much babysitting.

When Mum divorced soon after I was born she wanted to go out and make all these new friends. They say they never got away with the things I do now when they were my age. Also, because my mum's still looking after me Sal, the younger one, resents that Mum can't look after her new baby like other grandmothers do for nights and weekends.

Mathew, 22

Children will always find something to be embarrassed about their parents. I always realised mine were older than the parents of my friends by a good 15 years. The major problems really only started happening in my teens when I wanted to go and spend time with my friends. And I didn't have any brothers and sisters to diffuse some of the tension.

Having older parents doesn't distance one from them, but there are practical difficulties. I'm sure children of younger parents have similar difficulties, but perhaps age accentuates them. Being older can either lead to you being set in your ways like my mother. Or, on the other hand you can have perhaps mellowed out a bit and be more relaxed about things, like my father. My father has always been less authoritative. My mother was always overly protective.

Going to boarding school was a real liberation. And I'd spend as much of my holidays as I could with my friends because the prospect of staying with people who had wacky young parents was obviously enticing. They always seemed to be able to turn a blind eye to teenage smoking and drinking, while mine would always be despairing.

My rebellion always caused my mother pain. Perhaps if she'd been younger she would have had different expectations. She would have been more tolerant.

Having older parents doesn't necessarily make your family more secure. In fact, it can be less stable. In our case the latent strains which may have been overlooked in the earlier stages of their marriage surfaced. When my father retired and spent more and more time at home, my parents had more time to see each other. And they didn't like it. The marriage broke up.

People are products of their age. My father spent time in the front line during the war. He was wielding bayonets at the enemy at an age when my contemporaries were rolling joints and going 'Hey man!'

My parents made me read and play the piano. My mother was violently against television and we didn't have one until I was 12. Perhaps it has its advantages. I adore reading and wish I'd read more. But at the time I couldn't bear not being able to make my own decisions about it.

I was definitely a rebel.

LAST WORDS

Your children are not your children.
They are the sons and daughters of Life's longing for
  itself.
They come through you but not from you.
And though they are with you yet they belong not to
  you.
You may give them your love but not your thoughts,
For they have their own thoughts.
You may house their bodies but not their souls,
For their souls dwell in the house of tomorrow, which
  you cannot visit, not even in your dreams.
You may strive to be like them, but seek not to make
  them like you.
For life goes not backward nor tarries with yesterday.

From *The Prophet*, by Kahlil Gibran

REFERENCES

Barker, D.J. *Mothers, Babies and Disease in Later Life.* London: British Medical Journal Press, 1995.

Berryman, J. 'Perspectives on Later Motherhood'. In *Motherhood: Meanings, Practices and Ideologies,* ed. by Ann Phoenix *et al.* London: Sage Publications, 1991.

Bettelheim, Bruno. *A Good Enough Parent: A Book on Childrearing.* London: Thames and Hudson, 1987.

de Crespigny, Lachlan. *Which Test for My Unborn Baby: A Guide to Prenatal Diagnosis.* Oxford University Press, 1991.

Dix, C. *The New Mother Syndrome.* London: Unwin, 1986.

Ellmann, Mary. *Thinking About Women.* London: Virago, 1979.

Emerson, Sally. *A Celebration of Babies.* London: Blackie, 1986.

Expert Advisory Group. *Folic Acid and the Prevention of*

Foetal Deformities. London: HMSO, 1993.

Gaskin, Ina May. 'Late Bloomers: Giving Birth after Thirty-five'. In *The Birth Gazette*, 1986.

Holdford, Liz and Patrick. *The Better Pregnancy Diet*. London: Ebury Press, 1987.

Jackson, Deborah. *Three in a Bed: Why You Should Sleep With Your Child*. London: Bloomsbury, 1989.

Jain, C.M. *The Baby Challenge*. London: Tavistock/Routledge, 1990.

Keating, R. and Williams, E. 'Prenatal Screening for Down's Syndrome'. *British Medical Journal*: 303, 1991.

Kitzinger, Sheila. *Breastfeeding Your Baby*. London: Dorling Kindersley, 1989.

—. *Book of Pregnancy and Childbirth*. London: Michael Joseph, 1989.

—. *Ourselves as Mothers*. London: Transworld/Doubleday, 1992.

Lashford, Stephanie. *The Twelve Month Pregnancy*. Bath: Ashgrove Press, 1985.

Leach, Penelope. *Baby and Child*. London: Penguin, 1977.

Leap, Micky and Hunter, Billie. *The Midwife's Tale: An Oral History from Handywoman to Professional Midwife*. London: Scarlet Press, 1993.

Macarthur, Lewis and Knox. *Health after Childbirth*. London: University of Birmingham and HMSO, 1991.

References

McNeil, M., ed. *New Reproductive Technologies*. London: Macmillan, 1990.

Maitland, Sara. *Why Children?* Ed. by Dowrick and Grundberg. London: Women's Press, 1980.

Morris, Desmond. *Babywatching*. London: Jonathan Cape, 1991.

Noble, E. *Essential Exercises for the Childrearing Year*. Boston: Houghton Mifflin, 1988.

Olkin, S.K. *Positive Parenting Fitness*. New York: Avery, 1992.

'The Outcome of Pregnancies in Elderly Primigravidae'. Paper presented at the European Congress of Perinatal Medicine, Dublin, 1984.

Purves, Libby. *How Not to Be a Perfect Mother: The Crafty Mother's Guide to a Quiet Life*. London: Fontana, 1986.

Renfrew, Mary *et al*. *Bestfeeding*. Berkeley, California: Celestial Arts, 1990.

Rothman, Barbara K., ed. *Encyclopedia of Childbearing: Critical Perspectives*. Phoenix: Oryx, 1993.

—. *The Tentative Pregnancy: Prenatal Diagnosis and the Future of Motherhood*. New York: Viking, 1986.

Swift, Julia. *Shape Up During Pregnancy*. London: HarperCollins, 1992.

Thevenin, Tine. *The Family Bed: An Age Old Concept in Child Rearing*. New York: Avery, 1987.

Triswell, A.S. 'ABC of Nutrition: Other Nutritional Deficiencies in Affluent Communities'. *British Medical Journal*: 291, 1985.

Walker, Peter. *Baby Massage: Massage and Movement for Babies and Children*. London: Piatkus Books, 1995.

—. *Loving Baby Massage* (video): send SAE to PO Box 829, London W9 2W2 for further information.

Weston, Carol. *From Here to Maternity: Confessions of a First-Time Mother*. London: Little, Brown & Co., 1991.

USEFUL ADDRESSES

Active Birth Movement, 55 Dartmouth Park Road, London NW5 1SL. 0171 267 3006.

Association for Improvements in the Maternity Services (AIMS), 163 Liverpool Road, London N1 0RF. 0171 278 5628. Offers information, advice and support for prospective parents.

Association for Post-natal Illness, 25 Jerdan Place, London SW6 1BE. 0171 386 0868.

Association for Spina Bifida and Hydrocephalus, ASBAH House, 42 Park Road, Peterborough, Cambridge PE1 2UQ. 01733 555988.

Birthright, 27 Sussex Place, Regents Park, London NW6 6LS. 0181 960 5585.

British Pregnancy Advisory Service, Austy Manor, Wootton Wawen, Solihull, West Midlands B95 6BX. 01564 793225.

Brook Advisory Centres, Central Offices 153a East Street, London SE17 2SD. 0171 708 1234.

Centre for Pregnancy Nutrition, Sheffield University, Clinical Sciences Centre, Northern General Hospital, Herries Road, Sheffield S5 7AU. 01742 434343, ext. 4888. Eating for Pregnancy helpline: 01742 424084.

Child, PO Box 154, Hounslow, Middlesex TW5 0EZ. 0181 992 5522. Advice on fertility.

Cleft Lip and Palate Association (CLAPA), Hospital For Sick Children, Great Ormond Street, London WC1A. 0171 404 9200.

B. M. Cry-sis, London WC1N 3XX. 0171 404 5011. Offers support for parents of crying babies.

Cystic Fibrosis Research Trust, Alexandra House, 5 Blyth Road, Bromley, Kent BR1 3RS. 0181 682 4001.

Down's Syndrome Association, 153–155 Mitcham Road, London SW17 9PG. 0181 682 4001.

Equal Opportunites Commission, Overseas House, Quay Street, Manchester M3 3HN. 0161 833 9244.

Exploring Parenthood, Latimer Education Centre, 194 Freston Road, London W10 6TT. 0181 960 1678.

Family Planning Information Service, 27–35 Mortimer Street, London W1N 7RJ. 0171 636 7866.

Foresight (Association for the Promotion of Preconceptual Care), 28 The Paddock, Godalming GU7 1XD. 01483 427839. Offers advice on care, recurrent miscarriage, infertility and nutrition.

Freeline Social Security: 01800 666555. For free information on maternity entitlements.

Gingerbread, 35 Wellington Street, London WC2E 7BN. 0171 240 0953. Offers support for one-parent families.

Harris Birthright Research Centre for Foetal Medicine. Development of Obstetrics and Gynaecology, King's College School of Medicine, Denmark Hill, London SE5 8RX. 0171 924 0894/0714 and 0171 346 3040. A major NHS research and clinical unit for foetal diagnosis and therapy, highly experienced in prenatal work. In 1994 more than 13,000 patients benefited from its services. Over 20,000 scans carried out. A new Foetal Medicine Centre is currently being set up privately, all funds of which will go to fund research into foetal medicine.

Health Education Authority, Hamilton House, Mabledon Place, London WC1H 9TZ. 0171 387 3833.

Independent Midwives Association, 63 Mount Nod Road, London SW16 2LP.

Institute of Optimum Nutrition, Blades Court, Deodar Road, London SW15 2NV. 0181 877 9993.

International Cerebral Palsy Society, 19 Saint Mary's Grove, Chiswick, London W4 3LL. 0181 995 5721.

International Planned Parenthood Federation, Regent's College, Inner Circle, Regent's Park, London NW1 4NS.

Issue (National Fertility Association), St George's Rectory, Tower Street, Birmingham B19 3RL. 0121 359 4887.

Life Lifehouse, Newbold Terrace, Leamington Spa, Warwickshire CV32 4EA. 01926 421587/311667/316737. Counselling for homeless mothers; abortion counselling, including after termination of handicapped foetus.

La Leche League of Great Britain, BM 3424, London WC1 6XX. 0171 242 1278. Support for breastfeeding mothers.

Marie Stopes, 114 Whitfield Street, London W1P 6BE. 0171 388 4843. Well Woman and gynaecology clinics.

Maternity Alliance, 15 Britannia Street, London WC1X 9JP. 0171 837 1265. Information on preconceptual care, maternity rights and benefits.

Meet-a-Mum Association (MAMA), 5 Westbury Gardens, Luton, Bedfordshire OU2 7DW. 01582 422253.

Miscarriage Association, Clayton Hospital Northgate, Wakefield, West Yorkshire WF1 3JF. 01924 200799.

Mind (The National Association of Mental Health), 22 Harley Street, London W1N 2ED. 0171 637 0741.

Multiple Births Foundation, Queen Charlotte's Hospital, Goldhawk Road, London W6 0XG. 0181 748 4666, ext. 5201.

National AIDS Trust, 285 Euston Road, London NW1 3DN. 0171 383 4246.

National Childbirth Trust (NCT), Alexandra House, Oldham Terrace, Acton, London W3 6NH. 0181 992 8637. Network of teachers providing antenatal preparation, postnatal support and advice on breastfeeding.

National Council for One-Parent Families, 255 Kentish Town Road, London NW5 2LX. 0171 267 1361.

National Information for Parents of Prematures, The Sam Segal Perinatal Unit, St Mary's Hospital, Praed Street, London W2 1NY. 0171 725 1487.

National Network for Parents Under Stress (OPUS), 106 Godstone Road, Whyteleaf, Surrey CR3 0EB. 0181 645 0469.

Natural Family Planning Centre, Birmingham Maternity Hospital, Queen Elizabeth Centre, Edgbaston, Birmingham B15 2TG. Send an SAE and a request for leaflets or the name of a teacher in your area.

One Plus One (Marriage and Partnership Research), Central Middlesex Hospital, Acton Lane, London NW10 7NS. 0181 965 2367.

Relate (National Headquarters), Little Church Street, Rugby, Warwickshire. 01788 573241.

Royal College of Midwives, 15 Mansfield Street, London W1M 0BE. 0171 580 6523.

Scope (formerly the Spastics Society), 12 Park Crescent, London W1N 4EQ. 0171 636 5020.

Support After Termination of Pregnancy for Abnormality (SAFTA), 73–75 Charlotte Street, London W1P 1LB. 0171 631 0280. Helpline: 0171 631 0285.

Twins And Multiple Births Association (TAMBA), 51 Thicknall Drive, Pedmore, Stourbridge, West Midlands DY9 0YH. 01384 373642.

Women's Health and Reproductive Rights Centre, 52 Featherstone Street, London EC1Y 8RT. 0171 263 6200.

Working Mothers Association, 77 Holloway Road, London N7 8JZ. 0171 700 5771.

Women Returners Network, 8 John Adam Street, London WC2N 6EZ. 0171 839 8188.

Index